Who counts?
assessing mathematics
in Europe

Who counts?
assessing mathematics in Europe

Leone Burton

tb

Trentham Books

First published in 1994 by Trentham Books Limited

Trentham Books Limited
Westview House
734 London Road
Oakhill
Stoke-on-Trent
Staffordshire
England ST4 5NP

British Cataloguing in Publication Data
A catalogue record for this book is available from the British Library.

ISBN: 1 85856 011 X

Designed and typeset by Trentham Print Design Limited, Chester and printed in Great Britain by Bemrose Shafron Limited, Chester

Contents

Acknowledgement

This book is the outcome of a Colloquium, called *Differential Performance in Assessment in Mathematics at the end of Compulsory Schooling*, which was held in May, 1992 at the University of Birmingham, U.K., and generously funded by a grant from the European Commission. The editor, and participants/authors, wish to express their thanks to the Commission for their support both for the Colloquium and for the subsequent publication.

Acknowledgment

Notes on Contributors

Josette Adda specialised first in mathematical logic but for the past twenty-five years has been in mathematics education in France. She is Professor of Education at the Universite Lumiere-Lyon 2 and Director of Research in Didactics of Mathematics at Universite Paris 7. She is the French Co-ordinator of IOWME (International Organisation of Women and Mathematics Education) and member of *Femmes et Mathematiques*.

Liv Berge used to teach in lower secondary school in Norway but is now teaching in upper secondary school. Her main subjects are mathematics and science. Apart from her teaching interests, she is concerned about mathematics and gender.

Leone Burton is Professor of Education (Mathematics and Science) at the University of Birmingham, UK where she is trying her best to encourage members of under-represented groups to enter and succeed at higher education. She has published widely in the area of mathematical thinking, social justice and mathematics education, and assessment. Her books include *Thinking Things Through* (1984), and *Children Learning Mathematics: Patterns and Relationships* (1994). She edited *Girls Into Maths Can Go* (1986), and *Gender and Mathematics: An International Perspective* (1990). She was a joint author of *Thinking Mathematically* (1982) and of a primary programme, *HBJ Mathematics* (1990 onwards) which engages children with mathematics thematically. She was International Convenor of IOWME 1984-88. Her proudest achievement is her son, except that he has to take a lot of the responsibility for being A Good Companion. She likes playing and listening to baroque music.

Sean Close is a lecturer in mathematics education in St. Patrick's College, Dublin, Ireland. He is currently seconded (part-time) to the National Council for Curriculum and Assessment to work on the development of a new mathematics programme for primary schools. He is also involved in organising extra-curricular courses for mathematically able children and youth. He has co-authored a textbook series for primary schools and carries out research into children's mathematical thinking and performance.

Truus Dekker teaches mathematics in the Netherlands at a broad comprehensive school containing vbo through vwo. She was involved in the work of the COW (Commission for the development of mathematics education) as a representative of 'W*omen and Mathematics*'. Since 1990, at the Freudenthal Institute in Utrecht, she has contributed to the development of exams for four year course in vocation/four year course in general education mathematics.

Catherine Goldstein is researcher at the Centre National de la Recherche Scientifique (CNRS) in France. Her main interests concern number theory and the history of mathematics. She has been a member of *Femmes et Mathematiques* since its inception and was its President in 1991-92.

Barbro Grevholm is a senior lecturer in mathematics and mathematics education in the Malmö School of Education, Lund University, Sweden. She works with teacher education for all levels and in-service training. For many years she has been and still is to a smaller extent teaching mathematics and physics in upper secondary school. She has published books for compulsory school, upper secondary school and teacher education in mathematics and taken part in curriculum development, school book evaluation and development work. She began the network *Women and Mathematics* in Sweden.

Monica Varoy Haga works at Stavanger College of Education, Norway, teaching mathematics and informatics. Her main interests in the last few years have been in two areas, the use of computers in the teaching of mathematics and the study of what factors make pupils like or dislike the subject of mathematics. She is married, has two girls and two dogs. She likes reading books, articles, comics and newspapers, and really dislikes writing anything.

Kirsten Haastrup is a teacher of mathematics and other subjects from the first to the tenth grade in Denmark. As she wants to influence the discussions and trends in school mathematics, she is actively engaged in the mathematics teachers' organisation, being the leader locally and on the national committee. She is also an officially appointed external examiner of the final written and oral examinations at grades 9 and 10.

Maria Eugenia Jiménez works as a mathematics teacher in a secondary school in Madrid (Spain). Before that, she worked as a teacher educator for three years. She is a founder member of the Mathematics Teachers' Society of Madrid *'Emma Castelnuovo'* where she works organising meetings and conferences about mathematics education. She is now engaged in a working group about co-education and mathematics as a part of the activities of the Spanish Section of the IOWME, OECOM *'Ada Byron'*.

Gabriele Kaiser-Meßmer studied originally at Kassel University, the Federal Republic of Germany, in order to become a gymnasium teacher of mathematics and the humanities. After working for two years in school, she returned to the University and wrote a PhD on *Theoretical analysis and empirical research on application-oriented mathematics teaching* Since then, she has worked on the staff of Kassel University publishing several papers on the theme of her thesis. In 1992 she began her habilitation on international comparisons of teaching and learning of mathematics in context. Additionally, interest in the area of gender and mathematics education led to her founding, with others, the German subgroup of the International Organisation of Women and Mathematics Education.

Christine Keitel is Professor of Mathematics Education at the Free University of Berlin, Federal Republic of Germany. Trained as a mathematician and sociologist, she worked at the Max-Planck-Institute for Educational Research and Human Development in Berlin, at the IDM in Bielefeld, and at the Technical University of Berlin. Her main research interests are in curriculum development and comparative studies, analysis of the social use of mathematics, of attitudes and belief systems, on the history and current state of mathematics education in various countries. She is the current International Convenor of IOWME and Vice-President of the Commission Internationale pour les Etudes et l'Amelioration de l'Enseignement des Mathematiques (CIEAEM).

Marian Kollenveld is a member of the board of *'Women and Mathematics'* in the Netherlands. She teaches mathematics at NB and NB in the upper grades.

Leonor Cunha Leal is a lecturer at the School of Education in Setubal, Portugal where she teaches a course on mathematics education. She works on a research project on Teacher Education and Professional Development and her main interests are assessment and teacher education.

Lena Lindenskov is a teacher and a researcher, teaching mathematics and social science at grades 10 to 12 in Denmark. Her research interest is in students' conceptions and how different kinds of everyday knowledge influences mathematics learning in school. She is also engaged in gender issues.

Maria-Jesús Luelmo is a mathematics teacher in a secondary school in Madrid (Spain). Previously she worked in teacher education and curricular development. She actively participates in Spanish teachers' associations and is currently the President of the Spanish Section of IOWME, OECOM *'Ada Byron'* and Vice-President of the Mathematics Teachers' Society of Madrid *'Emma Castelnuovo'*. She has written books and articles about teaching and learning geometry and the use of manipulative materials in the classroom.

Kathleen Lynch is Co-ordinator of the Equality Studies Centre at University College Dublin, Ireland. This is an inter-faculty Centre involved in running Masters, PhD degrees and a diploma programme in equality studies. She is also a lecturer in sociology in the Education Department. Prior to working at UCD, Kathleen worked in the Educational Research Centre at St. Patrick's College, Dublin and in Sherrard House Hostel for Homeless Girls. She has published widely in the areas of education and sociology. She is joint editor of *Ireland: A Sociological Profile* (1986), author of *The Hidden Curriculum* (1989) and joint author of *Schools and Society in Ireland* (1993).

Joao Filipe Matos is Professor of Mathematics Education at the University of Lisbon, Portugal, where he teaches masters courses and pre- service courses in mathematics education, the use of technology and modelling. He is concerned with the role of cultural models which pupils bring to school and is working on a research project which aims to study the interface between these and real world problem situations.

Marja Meeder studied mathematics at the University of Amsterdam, specialising in mathematics education. After teaching in secondary schools for ten years, she has work on the staff of an institute for adult education in Amsterdam. In 1981 she initiated the Dutch organisation *'Women and Mathematics Education'* and published e.g. *'Vrouwiskunde'* (*'Girls in mathematics education'*; 1984) and *'Vriendelijke Wiskunde'* (1987). Since 1988 she has co-ordinated a project at the Freudenthal Institute developing a new mathematics curriculum for 12-16 year old students in the Netherlands. At the same time she has also been involved in a project *'Mathematics and Emancipation'* for the pre- and in-service training of teachers. She was co-author of *'Emancipatie ABC voor de wiskunde-les'* (an emancipation guide for mathematics practice; 1991). At the moment she works at the APS (an institute for educational studies) co-ordinating the implementation of the new mathematics curriculum mentioned above.

Marilyn Nickson is a research officer and primary adviser with the University of Cambridge Local Examinations Syndicate where she is involved in research related to the assessment and development of mathematics curricula. She has spent several years in mathematics teacher education, first at the University of Cambridge Department of Education and then at the Department of Education, Anglia Polytechnic University where she became Head of the Mathematics Section. Her recent publications include the joint editing of a book on 'Research into Social Perspectives of Mathematics Education' (with S Lerman) and 'The culture of the mathematics classroom: an unknown quantity?' in the *Handbook of Research on Teaching and Learning Mathematics* (ed. D Grouws).

Margita Nilsson is a senior lecturer in mathematics education in the Malmö School of Education, Lund University, Sweden. She has also worked as a teacher of mathematics in upper secondary school and with curriculum development in mathematics. In recent years, she has published textbooks for mathematics teacher education.

Elizabeth E Oldham is a lecturer in education at Trinity College, Dublin, Ireland. She has responsibility for mathematics and information technology education. She is also a part-time lecturer in an associated college of education which deals with primary education. Currently, she is seconded for two days per week to the National Council for Curriculum and Assessment as a second level Education Officer for Mathematics. Her involvement is with the development of courses for the age group 12-18 years. Her research interests are in the Curriculum Analysis Group of the Second International Mathematics Study for which she was the Irish National Research Co-ordinator and she has some involvement at national and international level with the Third Study.

Stephanie Prestage is currently a lecturer in mathematics education at the University of Birmingham, working on initial teacher education and professional development courses. Before moving to Birmingham she taught mathematics in London, latterly as Head of the mathematics department in a large mixed comprehensive school.

Leila Schneps is an American who has a research position in pure mathematics in the CNRS in France. Her research area is number theory. Although an undergraduate at Harvard University in the USA, she did her graduate studies in Paris and, as a female mathematician in France, became involved in the group *Femmes et Mathematiques* which was founded to support those women already in mathematics or thinking about entering it.

Fidela Velázquez is General Secretary of the Mathematics Teachers 'Isaac Newton' Canary Association and member of the Permanent Commission of the Spanish Federation of Mathematics Teachers Associations. She is also the Vice-President and founder member of the Spanish Section of IOWME. She is currently working in a secondary high school but taught in a primary school for several years. She has written books and articles about mathematics, participated in several congresses and meetings and is presently writing a book about curriculum and co-education as well as working in some co-education research projects with other members of '*Ada Byron*'.

CHAPTER ONE

Differential Performance in Assessment in Mathematics at the end of Compulsory Schooling: A European Comparison

Leone Burton

Background

In May, 1992, a Colloquium on Differential Performance in Assessment in Mathematics at the end of Compulsory Schooling was held at the University of Birmingham, UK, funded by a grant from the European Commission. The Colloquium was attended by pairs of participants from each of the following ten countries: Denmark, England, France, Germany, Ireland, the Netherlands, Norway, Portugal, Spain, and Sweden. Preparation for the Colloquium by each pair consisted in the detailing, in a paper, of the styles of assessment in mathematics within their country, where possible including documentary evidence on results differentiated by gender. Two objectives of the Colloquium were:

1. to document similarities and differences in styles of assessment of mathematics in the participating European countries, with respect to their impact on gender differentiated achievement;

2. to focus on the range of assessment styles represented, the contexts of assessment debates currently taking place, and the implications for achievement in mathematics.

Subsequent to the Colloquium, papers were written to reflect the discussions held and it is these papers which form the chapters of this book and have provided the substance for this comparative overview.

Introduction

At the present time, no detailed comparison of mathematics assessment in Europe exists and although decision makers tend, in principle, to acknowledge the benefits of sharing experience across national boundaries, in reality, (and certainly in the UK) this is only valued to the extent that it supports the current political imperative and fits within the cultural frame. In making the comparisons for this paper, I have been fascinated by how arbitrary are structures which, from inside their respective countries, appear, in some cases, to be 'immutable' in that they seem fixed by culture. In other cases, experiments are designed within another fixed cultural climate which surrounds the nature, role and expectations pinned to assessment, in particular of mathematics. I hope to draw out these similarities and differences across cultures in an attempt to clarify what are substantive issues for many mathematics educators, to indicate the arbitrariness of much of the practice, and to identify cross-cultural research issues which remain to be debated.

The chapter begins with a system-wide comparison of schooling. This is followed by a comparison of mathematics curricula which pays particular attention to the philosophical differences underlying curricular approaches (see Burton, 1992a). In discussing curriculum, I start first with a perspective on syllabus, then on pedagogy and finally on assessment (see Burton, 1992b for a discussion of this model of curriculum). This section is followed by an overview of the assessment debate in each of the countries. The final section looks at gender-differentiated performance and what evidence has been gathered in the ten countries. What can this tell us about poor mathematical performance in general? The paper concludes by raising research questions which result from the preceding analysis.

System-wide comparison

The table below demonstrates the wide variation in educational systems. All ten counties have universal, free, compulsory schooling. But as this chart makes clear, children may compulsorily start school in one country as young as 4 or, in another, as old as 7 years, and may leave school as

	First School	Second school	Post-Comp.	School Type
DENMARK 9 yrs 7-16	all through schools	grades 1-9	grades 10-12	vocational, commercial, pre-university
ENGLAND AND WALES 11 yrs 5-16	Reception + Years 1-6	Years 7-10	Years 11-12	secondary comprehensive grammar (acad.)
FRANCE 10 yrs 6-16	Preparatory + Elementary 1,2+ Intermediate	Sixth — First	Terminal	
GERMANY 9-10 yrs 6-16	grades 1-4 in primary or special needs school	grades 5-9/10	grade 10-12/13	Gymnasium, Gesamtschule or Berufsschule (vocational school)
IRELAND 11 yrs 4-15	Ages 4-12	Ages 12-15	Ages 15-18	
THE NETHERLANDS 12 yrs 4-16	Ages 4-12	4 tracks Grades 1-4 (2) Grades 1-5 (1) Grades 1-6 (1)		pre-university, higher vocational, general education, vocational
NORWAY 9 yrs 7-16	Grades 1-6	Grades 7-9	Ages 16-18	upper secondary
PORTUGAL currently 6 yrs 6-12 from 1995 9yrs 6-15	Grades 1-4 Grades 5-6 Grades 1-4 Grades 5-6	Grades 7-9	Grades 7-12 Grades 10-12	pre-university/ technical professor
SPAIN currently 8 yrs 6-14 from 1995 10 yrs 6-16	Ages 6-14 Ages 6-12	Ages 12-16	Ages 16-18	pre-university vocational/ professional
SWEDEN 9 yrs 7-16	Grades 1-6	Grades 7-9	Grades 10-12	upper secondary

3

early as their 13th or as late as their 16th birthday. Choices, with respect to differentiated provision, must be made as young as 10 years in Germany, or 12 years in the Netherlands or as old as 16 years in Denmark and Sweden. Such choices between, for example, vocational, commercial and academic schooling, can establish the future pattern of adult lives and distribute social opportunities without any clear evidence as to their efficacy. Furthermore, depending upon which side of a state boundary you live, compulsory schooling can currently last for anything from six to twelve years. This is in a Community which intends to remove national impediments to movement across states. Additionally, there is another cultural issue which makes a considerable difference to the reading of this chart. Some states believe in the retention of pupils to repeat a grade, others promote children by age cohort, and in some they do both. Thus, for example, in France where 50% of students repeat at least one class, all school leavers will not necessarily have completed the same number of different grades on leaving compulsory school. This could be an immediate discriminator between those pupils maintaining a high-achieving educational profile, up to the Baccalaureate, and those for whom school provides a poor preparation for adulthood. The same issue is a concern in Portugal. By comparison, every 16 year old leaving school in England will not only have spent eleven years in school but will have progressed through school with her/his age cohort as far as Year 11. In the Netherlands, age progression operates in the primary sector; repetition of class is possible in the secondary.

Curriculum Concerns

Let us turn to issues of curriculum. What is the driving curricular philosophy which influences public policy and its implementation in schools? In both France and England, it is top-down and positivist — a view of the sacrosanct nature of mathematical knowledge and skills necessary for high achievement, which accords high status to mathematics and science. In France, at the end of 2nd class (i.e. about the age of fifteen years for a high-achieving non-repeater), a curriculum choice is made which will lead to a specific Baccalaureate, scientific, literary or technical/vocational. One year later, one of seven options is chosen, the most prestigious being option C, mathematics/science. Syllabi are developed centrally. In England and Wales, mathematics is a compulsory subject of the National

4

Curriculum which is specified centrally in great detail on ten levels and across four (according to the latest proposal) Attainment Targets applicable to the years of compulsory schooling. The specification relies upon an hierarchical conception of the curriculum although the detail does not match this conception, with gaps and leaps in content causing teachers both concern and amusement. This is confounded by the relativist advice which is issued to teachers which contains such statements as:

> Each person's 'map' of the network and of the pathways connecting different mathematical ideas is different, thus people understand mathematics in different ways. (Department of Education, 1991, para 2.1, p. C1)

> The teacher's job is to organise and provide the sorts of experiences which enable pupils to construct and develop their own understanding of mathematics, rather than simply communicate the ways in which they themselves understand the subject. (*ibid*, para 2.2, p. C2)

An hierarchical view of the discipline can be found in Ireland, too, where there is a core curriculum for mathematics, a compulsory subject, but offered at three levels, A, B and C. In Spain, a single curriculum is being put into place and Sweden has a centralised system and a national curriculum. Of course, the content of each of these prescribed, core curricula is very different even though the assumption within each state is that there is only one mathematics. What is much more uniform is the didactic style which dominates the teaching of mathematics, a style which is consistent with the absolutist view of 'delivering' a discipline consisting of essential knowledge and skills.

However, the same clashing philosophies, to which I drew attention above with reference to England and Wales, are in evidence in the practices in other European countries. Let me put this clash into a clearer perspective. Ask many non-mathematicians about the nature of the discipline and they reply in terms of knowledge and skills which are seen as objective and certain, logically and hierarchically connected, and technologically potent. This is the positivist paradigm which pervades thinking about mathematical curricula in many, although not all, countries. For example, the English philosopher, A.J. Ayer wrote:

Whereas a scientific generalisation is readily admitted to be fallible, the truths of mathematics and logic appear to everyone to be necessary and certain. (1946, p.72)

However, Imre Lakatos challenged the certainty:

Everybody looks enviously at the alleged unanimity of mathematicians; but in fact there is a considerable amount of controversy in mathematics. Pure mathematicians disown the proofs of applied mathematicians, while logicians in turn disavow those of pure mathematicians. (1983, p.61)

And disagreeing with the ready admissibility of the fallible nature of science, Harry Collins and Trevor Pinch explained that science propounds the same absolutist myths as mathematics:

When something goes wrong with science, the scientific community reacts like a nest of ants with an intruder in their midst. Ants swarm over an intruder giving their lives for the nest; in the case of science it is human bodies that are sacrificed: the bodies of those responsible for the 'human error' that allowed the problem to arise... By contrast, our conclusion is that human 'error' goes right to the heart of science, because the heart is made of human activity... One cannot ask of scientists and technologists that they be no longer human, yet only mythical automata... could deliver the sort of certainty that scientists have led us to expect of them. (1993, p.142)

Mathematics, then, is no less of a human creation than any other discipline and, as such, is prey to the same subjectivities of individuals and cultures. Some mathematicians, themselves, recognise this relativism:

Mathematics is not a structure of steel resting on the bedrock of objective reality, but gossamer floating with other speculations in the partially explored regions of the human mind. (Kline, 1972, p.129)

We could look at these developments in mathematics simply as the onwards and upwards march of truth in the service of intellectual progress. But to do so hides the societal imagery within which numbers and other mathematical notions have been conceptualised, and the very interesting processes of social negotiation through which one cultural image for thinking about mathematical concepts comes to replace another. (Harding, 1986, p.50/51)

6

Far from being the absolute, clearly-defined and prescriptive discipline that exists where a national curriculum is imposed, mathematics is understood by many as the relativistic study of patterns and relationships in which the actively engaged student, rather than the content, is central to the enquiry. This view of mathematics learning can often be found in the support material produced for teachers such as that already mentioned from England and Wales. However, it is also the philosophy which underpins the Danish mathematics curriculum, and one of the two (optional) curricula on offer in the Netherlands. Known as Mathematics A, the approach to mathematics in this curriculum is through the applicable, rather than the reproducible. Additionally, in Spain, the reformed curriculum emphasises that mathematics is an essential skill for understanding your own situation, communicating with others and solving daily life problems more than a preparation for later studies. It values mathematical language and ideas, promotes mathematics in context and the learning of general mathematical strategies for problem solving. In order to evaluate the power of this rhetoric, we must examine how consistent it is with the official view taken on assessment.

Assessment

DENMARK	Grades 1-8 all assessment schools based. End grade 9 — optional Ordinary Final Exam consisting of 1 basic skills 50 question test (1 hr.) and 1, 4 hr., problem- solving test. End grade 10 — optional Ordinary Final Exam *or* optional Advanced Final Exam consisting of 1, 4 hr., problem-solving test and 1 oral teacher prepared exam. The end grade 9 and 10 tests are prepared centrally by team of practising teachers and Test Unit.
ENGLAND	Centrally prepared compulsory written tests at 7, 11, 14 years. Optional 16 plus examination offered by choice out of 5 (private) examination groups. Groups centrally monitored. 3 tiers of entry: high, intermediate, foundation.
FRANCE	Optional Baccalaureate at end of Terminal Class set regionally by teacher teams. Diagnostic testing of all students entering certain classes, e.g. 1990 Elementary 2 and Sixth Class

GERMANY	All curricula state-based. All assessment school, teacher-based and continuous, including tests, written 'classworks' and orals except in a few states which have centralised final school exams. Access to University can be through set tests.
IRELAND	Junior Certificate examination (15 years) Mathematics compulsory. Optional Leaving Certificate examination at end of second level. Mathematics optional: higher, ordinary or ordinary alternative.
THE NETHERLANDS	Compulsory test at 12 years to decide secondary tract but 14 subject curriculum compulsory for all pupils until 16 years. All pupils take national, standardised written tests different for each track. Vocational and general track — multiple choice and open problems. Higher vocational and pre-university — no multiple choice. Diploma achieved by averaging national test result with average of teacher-awarded grades from internal tests during final school year.
NORWAY	School-based assessment. Pupils included in process. No marks given. Many and different forms of informal assessment used in grades 1- 6 Centralised (optional) tests given at grades 7 and 9. Assessments in grades 7-9 formal, school-based.
PORTUGAL	Assessments formative, continuous, and school-based. Also summative termly, awarded approved/not approved scale 1-5. Repetition for those not approved. Set, marked by teachers.
SPAIN	One centralised curriculum (in secondary after 1995). No external tests other than University-set entrance examinations. Assessment continuous, seen as part of teaching and learning, diagnostic.

SWEDEN	National Curriculum End of compulsory schooling, pupils awarded a school Certificate, grades 1-5. No formal examinations, but compulsory participation in national standardised test end grade 9 to provide comparative information to schools on gradings. On paper short questions, answers only demanded, one paper theme-based. Grades 7-9, choice of general or advanced maths course Post-compulsory — 4 possible mathematics courses University Entrance Examination includes multiple choice items.

As can be seen, the ten countries view assessment in different ways. There is a group, Denmark, Norway and Spain, who preach and practice a relativist approach to learning using school-based education supported by teacher driven assessment. Then there are those whose absolutist curriculum is matched with a test-driven assessment system, England and Wales being a clear example but France and Ireland also falling into this category. Ireland's attempt to introduce more flexible assessment styles has apparently foundered due to lack of resources (see below). The hierarchical view of learning present in centralised curricula is reinforced, in the case of France, by the practice of retaining some pupils to repeat a year. Portugal also practices retention, and like the Netherlands and Sweden, has a centralised mathematics curricula but, in different ways, these three countries offer examples of the mixing of rhetorics. The Netherlands is very hierarchical in its school organisation, but relativistic in the way in which it approaches the mathematics curriculum. Probably more than any other European country, with its Mathematics A secondary syllabus the Netherlands has experimented with a wide variety of innovative, pupil-friendly assessment styles that challenge learning rather than maintaining mathematical mysticism. Nonetheless, the option of Mathematics B, the purist approach to mathematics required by the University mathematics gatekeepers, is still retained and the relativism of the curriculum approach is embedded in an hierarchical structure. Portuguese documentation of its centralised curriculum emphasises construction, rather than absorption, of knowledge. Active and intuitive approaches to mathematics learning are recommended; modelling of real-world situations, problem-solving and the incorporation of technology into class-room activity is proposed, and interdisciplinary approaches to mathematics learning are part of the timetable. The system, however, is strongly led by summative assessments although these are set and marked by teachers. Teachers' education and experience is dominated by individualism antagonistic to the new demands. Germany, too, practices teacher-led assessment. Within a system which is highly differentiated by school category and is very assessment oriented, German assessments are school-based and in the hands of the teachers for both setting and marking. In practice, despite teachers holding this power, assessment of mathematics is test-dominated. In Sweden, a centralised curriculum and hierarchical choice of general or advanced mathematics courses at grade 7 conflicts with a rhetoric which maintains that marks should not depend only on tests and that teachers should be wary of overvaluing easily obtained results. Furthermore, the longer of the two standardised test papers is theme-based (see Appendix to Chapter 11). The only diplomas awarded in compulsory school are school-based and there is no publication of tests or results.

What do we learn from this comparison? The almost universal rhetoric about the nature of mathematics learning which is to be found in the mathematics education literature supports a relativist, social-constructivist philosophy which values active, enquiry-based learning in a resource-rich environment. Numerous research studies bear out the efficacy of this approach to the learning of mathematics. From this perspective, mathematics is less a static, stipulated syllabus than the result of dynamic engagement with challenging questions which provoke judgements about quantity, construction and patterning while recognising and valuing qualitative constraints. In the documentation of most of the ten countries this rhetoric has permeated at some level. In the case of Denmark, Norway and Spain it contributes to the style and/or the content of the curriculum, where I understand by the curriculum the totality of syllabus, pedagogy and assessment. In the case of the seven other countries, evidence can be found of its influence but that influence is in conflict with an absolutist approach to mathematics knowledge in the syllabus, and, frequently, in the so-called objective testing which is the basis of the assessment system. In the Netherlands, the split exists in the division between two optional syllabi, but also in the retention of multiple choice testing, a known gender discriminator, for the perceived less-able pupils within the hierarchical tracking of secondary schooling.

The result of this philosophical conflict between rhetoric and behaviour is that the pervading absolutist vision of mathematics retains its power to mystify and to exclude. A large number of pupils, at worst, carries the stigma of mathematical failure and many more have their potential interest or confidence in the subject eroded. Mathematics ends up being used to fulfil non-mathematical purposes such as the distribution of scarce resources.

The debate on assessment

Interestingly, across all ten countries an assessment debate has been part of their most recent decision-making in education. But that debate takes very different forms, country to country.

In Denmark, the concerns have been located in strengthening the relativistic aspects of mathematics learning especially by finding innovative ways to assess pupils' experiences, experiments, discussions, etc. Students now, for example, are more involved in the collection, analysis and evaluation of data in the light of different applied statistical tools, than in the learning of these tools in isolation from their use. The incorporation of an oral, school-based examination further supports reflection on within-school activity. In Spain, too, the official position is that assessment must be as useful to pupils as to their teachers and that it must evaluate a broader range of behaviours than simply the reproduction of knowledge or skills. However, teachers are faced with many questions such as: how to assess attitudes, do school situations transfer to daily life, and how to evaluate the role of group as well as individual work.

Political concerns dominate the assessment debate in England and Wales, Ireland and Sweden. In England and Wales, conflict with teachers has been induced by the government's intention to test all children at four points in their compulsory schooling and by the rapidity with which a National Curriculum and its associated testing structure have been introduced. In Ireland resources have not been made available, particularly for in-service teacher education, nor has payment for the increased demands made on teachers by continuous assessment. This has led to a similar deadlock between government and teaching force and to consequent constraints on the proposed shifts from traditional external examinations to a wide range of assessment techniques such as oral, aural, practical and project work. In Sweden, decentralisation, and evaluation based on formulated objectives are at the centre of debate. This might appear to be a contrast to the political/economic arguments in England and Ireland. However, underneath the debate is the scarce resource issue and the particular political position which dictates managerial decentralisation as a solution.

These arguments are also to be found in Norway where debate on assessment has been integral to debate on educational policy. For example, the decision in 1974 to abolish marks in grades 1-6 was made because they were seen to be incompatible with such educational aims as pupil-oriented learning. The result was a broadening of styles of informal assessment and the inclusion of pupils' perspectives as a necessary part of the process. However, marks continued to be used to evaluate student performance in grades 7-9. More recently the debate has continued and involved post-compulsory schooling and a more technocratic and value-for-money approach.

In Portugal, education has undergone considerable re-thinking since the middle 1980s. However, teacher control over the decision to retain or promote a pupil has remained inviolable so far and the debate on styles of assessment has continued. In 1992, a new law introduced changes with respect to the involvement of students and their parents in the process, the introduction of a portfolio to record basic education, the treatment of retention as exceptional and the broadening of assessment into both formative and summative stages, with only the latter informing the decision on progress.

In Germany there is on-going discussion among didacticians about broadening both assessment modes and practices, and particularly developing informal, criteria-based assessment styles in order to overcome the constraints imposed by standardised testing. In addition, reunification has provoked debate about assessment, the education of teachers and the role of schooling.

The shift from mechanistic to applicable mathematics in the new curricula in the Netherlands has been matched by a careful consideration of how assessment fits these expectations of learning. The developers established five principles for assessment. It should:

1. improve learning;
2. test what is known rather than uncover what is not;
3. focus on the process of the curriculum objectives, not their products;
4. evaluate the quality of the test in ways other than objective scoring;
5. fit into the usual school practice.

Inevitably, this led to a much closer involvement with the effects that some curricular approaches have on the performance of different groups of pupils and the introduction of a wide range of new assessment strategies such as:

1. the two-stage task, in which the first stage was a restricted-time written test. The second stage, for which the learner received back the marked test, was the production of a long essay, without time restrictions, commenting on and correcting the first stage paper.
2. the take-home task, in which students were given the choice of one out of five tasks, could work alone or in pairs, and produced an extended report.
3. the open essay task which contained questions covering many areas.
4. the oral task, consisting of a discussion on subjects designated in advance, a discussion of an article provided to students twenty minutes earlier, or a discussion on a take-home task after completion.

The following comments were made:

1. Girls perform less well than boys on restricted-time written tests.
2. Girls perform more or less the same as boys on oral tasks or take-home tasks.
3. From the above, one is tempted to advise more oral and take-home tasks in order to offer girls fairer chances.
4. Oral test results have a somewhat higher correlation with restricted-time written test results than do take-home tasks.
5. Students perform best with take-home tasks. The constructive and productive aspects seem to offer students a fair chance to show their abilities (creativity, reflection, etc.). Positive testing is at its optimum in this way.

13

We started our exploratory study on alternative tasks because of the fact that the restricted-time written tests as carried out by the teachers did not meet the intentions and goals of Mathematics A... (which) is strongly process-oriented; the mathematisation process needs time to develop, time to generate creative and constructive thoughts. These 'higher' goals are not easily operationalise with timed tests. (de Lange, 1987, p.260)

On the other hand, in France it is now socially unacceptable to suggest that girls are less capable at mathematics than boys and there have been a number of national and regional campaigns designed to consider the different outcomes of schooling which the top-driven academic curriculum induces. System-wide tests at different levels demonstrated that fathers whose work does not require a high level of education are less likely to have daughters doing mathematics. This leads me to the third, and final, basis for comparison of the ten countries.

Differences in performance

It is a uniform experience across the ten countries discussed here, but also more widely, that achievement in mathematics is biased in favour of white, middle-class males. This bias takes different forms. In some countries, achievement appears to match population distribution but, on closer examination, the females are more likely to achieve middle grades, the males to be represented at the top and the bottom extremes. In other countries, research indicates that performance of females in assessment tasks appears to deteriorate with age. However, this has not, to my knowledge, been examined from the perspective of assessment styles except where there has been a monitoring of innovation. The results of such monitoring lead to the conclusion that achievement in mathematics is affected not only by classroom experiences, social attitudes and expectations, and the experience of persistent prejudice but also by reaction to more deeply rooted conceptions about the nature of the discipline, and its consequent pedagogy and assessment.

Again, information is scattered and inconsistent.

DENMARK	No formal data interrogation or research

ENGLAND & WALES	Considerable data collected. Two major issues for differentiation: 3 tiers of entry to 16+ examination, and the effects of coursework. For higher tier of entry, grades A-D can be obtained, from intermediate tier, grades C-F, foundation tier, grades E-G. Grades C and above necessary to further education. Proportionally more females entered for intermediate or foundation. Decision on entry taken by class teachers. In 1990, 8.6% males, 5.8% females achieved an A, 10.3% males, 8.4% females a B, 24% males, 23% females a C. Research on the achievement of females by style of examination (i.e. proportion of continuously teacher-assessed coursework included) shows that the higher proportion of coursework, the better the females achieve. Govt decision to restrict coursework to maximum of 20%.

FRANCE	Data exists on baccalaureate results particularly with reference to entry to Grandes Ecoles. Prior to 1986, each Grande Ecole had sex-separated entrance competitions and courses approx 33% female. Post 1986, open competition led to drop in female entry to 10% at best. Competitive entry of C bac students to preparatory classes for Grandes Ecoles, 18% female, to scientific sections of Universities, D bac students 30% females. Females tend to drop out or down.

GERMANY	Lack of survey studies and detailed analysis of assessment results especially constrained by the teacher-based organisation. Fewer girls than boys opt for high achievement maths and science courses in secondary or start university studies in these subjects. At Gymnasium, girls' achievement in maths lower, in languages and humanities higher. Studies show girls better behaved, harder working, more industrious, cause fewer disciplinary problems.

IRELAND	Considerable data collected. 55.2% pupils at end of 2nd level are female. Males outnumber females in 3rd level and distribution is sex-stereotyped (e.g. 15% entrants to engineering female). Research evidence shows deterioration in performance with female pupils out-performing males until the end of lst level

where males take over. Secondary higher socio-economic status pupils out-perform lower SES pupils, but gender differences greater in the higher than the lower SES groups. Data from the Junior and Leaving Certificate examinations show a greater proportion of males passing and gaining grade C or above but that the gap is narrowing. It is, however, questionable how comparable are the different data bases and, consequently, their results.

THE NETHERLANDS	Introduction of Mathematics A monitored from a gender perspective. More female students choose Mathematics A but Mathematics B is necessary to a technical/scientific further education. Choice might therefore be operating against female interests.
NORWAY	Data on differentiation of test results collected but not made public. What is available confirms patterns observed elsewhere. Particularly in post-compulsory schools, males enter with better marks and are more likely to continue with mathematics than females. Females' marks deteriorate in the first year of upper secondary school.
PORTUGAL	No formal data interrogation or research.
SPAIN	Formal school 54% female, vocational school 46% female. 50% University students female, subject base differentially distributed e.g. 60% female in literary/humanistic disciplines, 48% in scientific where 15% engineering, 30% architecture, 72% psychology. Female mathematics students intend to enter teaching, males business or industry. Examination of University entrance shows female school marks better than male; entrance test marks worse for all students than school grades but overall average worse for females. Females' attitudes to mathematics in school poorer even where results are better. Where females in experimental schools with non-formalistic styles of teaching and learning, females perform better and have higher expectations.

SWEDEN	National tests and results not released publicly. Research indicates males score higher than females but the inverse is true of school results. Fewer low SES males choose advanced mathematics course but twice as many males as females choose advanced mathematics. When Science becomes optional (grade 7), chosen by 30% males, 3% females.

What conclusions can be drawn from this? First, it is evident that changes in a relativist direction in learning and assessing styles lead to improvements in the performance of females. The evidence with respect to coursework from England and Wales and the alternative syllabi in the Netherlands reinforces the idea that pupil ownership, involvement and control over the learning material motivate and empower learners of mathematics. From Denmark we are told that females respond positively to a more personal involvement with mathematics, to active, enquiry-based methods, to collaborative group work and a broader syllabus. It is inevitable, then, to conclude that female rejection of mathematics either in option choice or by safe, poorer performance is an indication of a deeper rejection of both what mathematics is taught and of how it is taught and consequently assessed. I believe that we could learn a lot by asking why it is that female students, across states, succeed at language studies rather than dismissing these studies as less important or more responsive to reproductive learning. On the contrary, reproductive learning patterns used so extensively in mathematics classrooms are rejected by females who thrive when learning in the more open, challenging, discursive and difficult language and literature environments. But in many countries we have failed to convince teachers, and in some cases administrators and politicians, of this. Equally, those responsible for a reliance on measuring achievement as equivalent to test behaviour are failing to understand that these judgements are usually dependent upon performance in the least important and relevant aspects of mathematics. This is as true for achievement tests as it is for system-wide testing such as the International Mathematics Studies.

Second, options which are organised hierarchically do no favours to groups which are under-achieving. Whether this is a result of the prejudices of the teachers, the parents and the pupils themselves, or to do with differentiated curricular experiences is hard to say. But the results demonstrate that if there are perceived options which are more or less academic, more females will be found in the lower option group. And an hierarchically organised mathematics curriculum is a function of an absolutist curriculum perspective which maintains that differentiated performance in mathematics assessment currently demonstrated in so many countries.

Third, there is considerable literature and research experience which criticises traditional examination techniques from a number of perspectives. They do not provide information on the important aspects of mathematics learning, they devalue the teacher's role, they demotivate pupils generally and discriminate against those pupils who refuse to be forced to compete against the clock for results the value of which does not equal the effort. When will we move to assessment styles closer to those described by Glaser, where teachers are:

> adept at developing instructional situations in which significant aspects of students' thinking and problem solving can be observed, assessed and constructively guided ...it would be poor practice to assess only declarative knowledge. Rather assessment activities would involve the use of knowledge and skill for problem solving and reasoning or the learning of new information and, consequently, the results of learning would be seen by students as foundations for further growth and accomplishment (1990, p.482/3).

However, evidence from countries such as Germany, which does trust teachers enough to leave summative assessment in their hands, demonstrates that those teachers abuse their power, relying heavily upon the reproduction of declarative knowledge in unseen, paper and pencil tests and resisting efforts to introduce more innovative, equitable practices.

One can only conclude that there is no evidence to suggest that females cannot achieve at mathematics. However, there is a lot of evidence to suggest that, until the discipline of mathematics is perceived differently and consequent changes are made to how it is learnt and assessed, females will continue to reject mathematics as an appropriate study. Female rejection is an indicator not only of the exclusion of that group from a wide range of social roles, but more broadly to a widespread societal pattern. Alongside female rejection goes 'poor performance' by other groups such as ethnic minorities or low SES pupils. When societies recognise a need for mathematically competent citizens and a shortage of those who can meet the demands of industry and commerce, a new interest is awakened in persuading females, and other under-represented groups, to re-engage with mathematics. However, without more energy being given to interrogating the nature, and consistency, of the mathematics, its pedagogy and assessment, it seems to me that such campaigns are unlikely to alter, fundamentally, the number of those persisting with the discipline.

Conclusions

It is, I think, surprising that different European states have such differing educational practices. While I would not want to argue for uniformity, it would be interesting to see some Europe-wide comparative research on the social implications of the differences which have been highlighted in this chapter. The lack of a European database, or even state databases in some cases, makes it very difficult to do comparative research and certainly to look at policy implications. Not only are there differences in starting and finishing ages of compulsory schooling, in retaining or progressing of age-cohorts, and in comprehensive or optional choices of subjects of interest. Also, within mathematics itself, we have no comparative information which maps the different results of different assessment styles or even of the same assessment style. Only the International Mathematics Studies apply the same technique cross-culturally but, in doing so, they do not engage with the implications of style or content. With reference to the Second International Mathematics Study,

> between-country gender differences are often greater than within-country differences and... (those) that do exist are not consistent across all the participating countries. (Burton, 1990, p.6)

France, in particular, has run national and regional attitudinal change programmes. Similar efforts have been made elsewhere, although not on a national scale, but results conflict in terms of their efficacy. The driving force for such campaigns are demographic shifts which expose economic need. This need is often to do with shortage of well-qualified teachers, where well-qualified must mean able to meet new demands and to re-perceive mathematics, its learning and teaching. Such campaigns need to be carefully monitored, a difficult task given the potential interdependency of short and long-term effects and the nature of the data which is not simply about numbers of registrants but also about attitudes.

Many of the countries discussed collect no gender differentiated data or deliberately do not make such data public. I am left with the sense of lack of any public policy on mathematics, assessment and equity. The formulation of such policy, together with mechanisms for dissemination, needs research.

Detailed consideration of different styles of assessment and the sharing of approaches to innovation from one country to another are long overdue. For example, the differentiated effects of multiple-choice testing in mathematics are now well-established in many states but this information, apparently, has failed to permeate some national and international fora. At the same time, do these effects persist across disciplines?

Where different school types exist, there is meagre evidence on their effects. Comparative case study material would be of benefit here to a more considered judgement about styles of schooling and the learning of disciplines such as mathematics.

Some work exists on the effect on learner behaviour of teacher beliefs. Cross-cultural studies, particularly where there are clashing public belief systems, are urgently required.

The analysis in this chapter has exposed the confusions underlying many curriculum practises in some European countries. Calls for pupil-centred, learner-friendly, socially-appropriate school experiences sit uncomfortably next to content-dominated, hierarchically organised absolutist syllabi or test-driven assessment systems. In the end, the power remains with the distribution of overt rewards and not with the possibly more enriching classroom experiences. Teachers are put under enormous pressure to conform with the demands of external controls, rather than persist with their own knowledge and intuitions about their pupils' learning. Despite widespread reaffirmation in the educational literature, therefore, on the powerful effects of learner autonomy, the success achieved when pupils are challenged rather than fed information, the unacceptable differences which result from hierarchically organised syllabi, classrooms and assessment techniques, it is clear that many European countries remain firmly committed to a style of teaching and assessing mathematics which is neither socially equitable nor a fair reflection of mathematics itself.

References

Ayer, A.J. (1946) *Language, Truth and Logic,* London: Gollancz.

Burton, L. (1990) (Ed.) *Gender and Mathematics: An International Perspective,* London: Cassell

Burton, L. (1992a) Who assesses whom and to what purpose? in M. Stephens and J. Izard (Eds) *Reshaping Assessment Practice: Assessment in the Mathematical Sciences under Challenge,* Hawthorn: Australian Council for Educ. Research.

Burton, L (1992b) Evaluating an 'entitlement curriculum': mathematics for all? in *The Curriculum Journal,* Vol.3, No.2, pp. 161-9.

Collins, H. & T. Pinch (1993) *The Golem,* Cambridge: University Press.

de Lange Jzn, J. (1987) *Mathematics Insight and Meaning,* Utrecht: OW&OC.

Department for Education, U.K. (1991) Non-statutory guidance to *Mathematics in the National Curriculum 5-16,* London: HMSO.

Glaser, R (1990) Toward New Models for Assessment in *International Journal for Educational Research,* Vol.14, No. 5.

Harding, S. (1986) *The Science Question in Feminism,* Milton Keynes: Open University Press.

Kline, M. (1972) *Mathematics in Western Culture,* Harmondsworth: Penguin.

Lakatos, I. (1983) *Mathematics, Science and Epistemology,* Cambridge: University Press.

CHAPTER TWO

Denmark

Lena Lindenskov
Kirsten Haastrup

In the Danish compulsory school arithmetic/mathematics is a compulsory subject in the first nine grades with four lessons per week. In grade 10 all subjects with the exception of what are called 'free class discussions' subjects are optional, yet all students opt for arithmetic/mathematics.

The syllabuses for school mathematics leave ample freedom for the teachers to make their own interpretations and choices. No nation-wide organised examinations are held during the first eight years in the compulsory school. Only at the end of grade 9 and again grade 10 is there a prescribed examination: in grade 9 a written one, in grade 10 both written and oral. The written ones are the same nation-wide, but the oral ones are organised and managed by the teacher her/himself. The teacher is responsible for guiding the students throughout their school life. It happens, but only rarely, that the teacher advises a student (and their parents) to repeat a grade. In these instances the reason given is that the student is immature for their age.

By the Education Act 1969, nine years of compulsory education was introduced. The students were split in grade 8, 9, and 10 into two levels. These splits were stopped from 1977, since when all students have been kept together from grade 1 through grade 10. This education policy is defined as non-streaming. It implies that the students of a class are taught together during their entire schooling, irrespective of their learning pre-requisites and other qualifications. (Only about two percent of the students suffer from severe physical or emotional disturbances that require special education in separate classes or special schools). From 1977 to August 1994, from grade 8 English, German, and arithmetic/mathematics, and from grade 9 physics/chemistry might be offered at two levels, basic and advanced. It has been up to each school and the administrative area where it belongs, (after consultations with teachers, students and parents) to decide whether this grouping should take place, and the trend has been that a constantly decreasing number of schools choose ability grouping. For instance, in 1990/91, 67% of all mathematics classes on grade level 8 were mixed ability classes taught according to the principle of non-streaming.

By the New Education Act — starting from August 1994 — all compulsory subjects will be taught in the same class throughout the nine years of compulsory schooling. Therefore it is now a main issue to discuss and improve *differentiated instruction*. Differentiated instruction means that all students in the class work towards the same general goals within the same topics; differentiated instruction means the utilisation of indi-viduals' potential within the whole class; and differentiated instruction means specific goals according to each individual's need and motivation.

Only 5% of the students from grade 9 and only 5% from grade 10 do not go directly into some further education. The distribution of students is as follows: From the 64,000 (approx.) students in grade 9, 21% continue from compulsory schooling directly into the Upper Secondary School, 2% continue directly into Basic Vocational Training, and 14% go directly into Commercial School, while 55% continue into grade 10. From the 34,000 (approx.) in grade 10, 23% continue directly into the Upper Secondary School, 66% continue directly into either Basic Vocational Training or into Commercial School.

Compared with the usual age level of school-starters in other countries, Danish children begin school a little later. The vast majority of Danish children enter the 1st grade in the calendar year when they attain 7 years. In fact children at the age of 5 years have access to the 1st grade, but very few parents make use of this possibility. Prior to grade 1 most children will attend a voluntary pre-school class, which provides play, socialisation and preparation of the children for learning. Some schools operate with 'co-ordinated-school-start' involving pre-school class, 1st and 2nd grades. The objective of teaching the students from all three levels in joint classes is to meet the needs of the individual child, to benefit from the diversity of characters and abilities, and to strengthen the social identity of the children.

From grade 1 through grade 7 an assessment of the individual student is maintained in all subjects save marking and without nation-wide, centrally set tests. The assessment is carried through in close co-operation between teacher, student, and parents. It lies with the individual teacher to supervise the personal and social development of each student. Twice during each academic year meetings are arranged for the purpose of keeping dialogue going between the individual teacher and parents in respect of their children. Furthermore, a minimum of one collective meeting for all parents is held every year. Quite often several meetings are held for the whole unit of students in one grade along with their parents and brothers/sisters, or they may all be invited to take part in a party, a picnic, or some other social gathering.

At the end of grade 9 the 'Ordinary Final Examinations' are held, consisting of two written examinations. One, of 1 hour duration, is a test in basic skills and contains fifty questions. The second one is a 4-hour-test in problem solving.

At the end of grade 10 the students again have the right to decide whether or not to sit for an examination. Additionally they may choose:

a) whether they want to sit for the 'Ordinary Final Examination' like that offered at the end of grade 9 containing a 1-hour test in basic skills and a 4-hour test in problem solution; or

b) whether they want to sit for the 'Advanced Final Examination' which contains both a written and an oral test. The written test is a 4-hour problem solving test, which includes more difficult questions than those in the Ordinary Final Examination. The oral examination lasts for 20 minutes, usually with 20 minutes preparation time.

The oral test is prepared by the individual teacher. The examination questions must cover the entire content of the reading matter offered, and each question should be posed in such a way as to include several aspects of the relevant subject. Not later than 10 days before the test is scheduled, the examination papers are forwarded to an external examiner who works at a different school. Before the test takes place, the teacher and the external examiner will meet and discuss the course of the examination and the form of the questions. Each pupil gets one mark.

Written tests, which function nation-wide, are prepared by an examination board set up by the test unit of the Ministry of Education. The chair is personally appointed, and the Ministry's educational adviser in mathematics is on the board as of right. Moreover, 6 personally selected teachers who teach the compulsory subject concerned are on the board. These teachers function as representatives of their colleagues in terms of sex and geographical disposition, small as well as large schools, municipal as well as private schools.

At the achievement test pupils are permitted to use practical aids such as compasses, ruler, angle meter, carbon paper, and blotter for calculation. Use of pocket calculator is not allowed. The answers are written directly onto the examination paper. At examinations in problem solving the students are also allowed to bring the collection of formulae and notes, they have written themselves during the year. Pocket calculators are allowed, except pre-programmed ones.

Immediately after the test the answers of the pupils are forwarded to an external examiner who assesses and marks the results. At the achievement test each correct answer is given 1 point. Marks for presentation are not given. Before the assessment of problem solving papers, the Ministry of Education will provide the examiners with guidelines on the marking policy indicating the maximum of points for each question. As a rule, the result is given as a maximum of points only provided that both the procedure and all answers are correct. If, for example, the result is correct but an algebraic description is missing, the answer will not achieve the highest point. If, conversely, the result is incorrect although the procedure is clearly correct, the mark of the answer is only reduced by a few points. With regard to conclusions, etc., it is difficult to set up concrete marking policies. The examiners have to make their own judgements.

Following the pre-assessment of answers, a mark conversion scale of the points is decided, although the marking of sets of problem solution allows for border points to count both up and down. It is for the examiner therefore, on the grounds of her/his collective impression of the set of questions, to fix the mark.

In addition to the assessment of sets of solutions to problems, marking for presentation is required, which indicates that both the way of writing and in particular the presentation of the mathematical work including text, algebraical terms, and clearly defined results are assessed.

The papers are then returned to the teacher who also assesses and marks the answers, whereupon the marks of the examiner and those of the teacher are compared. If they are in agreement, the student gets the mark agreed on, and if there is a margin of one point, the mark of the examiner will usually prevail. If there is a margin of two points, the average mark is chosen. Whenever a difference of opinion occurs between teacher and examiner regarding assessment, they will discuss the matter.

It is for the students to decide whether they want to sit for these tests. The data below show the number of students who sat for written examinations, and the sex distribution of the students in 1988:

At the end of grade 9, 95.7 % of the boys and 99.3% of the girls sat for the examination.

At the end of grade 10, 87.1% of the boys and 91.5 % of the girls sat for the examination.

These figures show greater interest from girls than from boys in the examination. But looking a little closer at *the choice between a) and b)* (the Ordinary or the Advanced Final examination we find more boys than girls took the more difficult test:

29.9% of the boys sit for a) (leaving) and 57.2% of the boys sit for b) (advanced).

41.1% of the girls sit for a) and 50.4% of the girls sit for b).

At schools which offer education at higher levels, students who seek entry are presumed to have sat for examinations, but it is not the custom that the marks of a student affect his/her admission to a school. When a student applies for access to an Upper Secondary School, the admission depends on the evaluation of the teachers at the previous school regarding the aptitude of the student. Therefore, any student who has been assessed 'apt' gains admission, whereas the student who is assessed 'not apt' is offered the possibility to sit for an admission test at the Upper Secondary School.

Moreover, adults have a good chance of attaining any missing proficiency test at a later time seeing that every large town runs a Centre for Adult Education which provides several kinds of education and offers examinations.

Over the last 7 years the written tests have been assessed by the Ministry of Education, and in the two most recent years the oral tests as well. The assessment report, of 30-40 pages, is sent to all schools in the country. It contains a gathering of the outcomes of the assessments, made by external examiners on what degree the examination questions met the objectives of education in arithmetic/mathematics.

Below is an extract of the 1991 assessment of the 4-hour problem solving test in 'The Ordinary Final Examination':

Problem Solution

Concerning a family's camping tour with tent:

The issues which were dealt with in the individual questions were as follows:

1. *Camping tour*   *Family economy, calculation of distances*
2. *Lilienhof*   *Family economy, currency transactions*
3. *Electricity consumption*   *Linear functions, percentage*
4. *Arrow game*   *Statistics*
5. *Swimming-pool*   *Structure, Pythagoras, area and volume*
6. *Superstructure*   *Scale, geometric figure, percentage, square root.*

In addition to these mathematical demands the set of questions was prepared in such a way that in between the questions the students were requested to solve problems in which they had no experience. By this procedure students were given the opportunity to prove their capacity to use different working methods and several forms of expression. The set of questions in general is described by the external examiners as well composed, with sufficient and diversified content relating to most of the issues which are incorporated in the education of the subject in compliance with the curriculum for the 8th and 9th grades. The topic is relevant as it 'speaks' to the students, and it is considered significant that they experience some connection between Mathematics and 'real life' at the

examination, which is the last contact that many of the students have with the subject in Primary and Lower Secondary School.
Task 6 on Superstructure was:

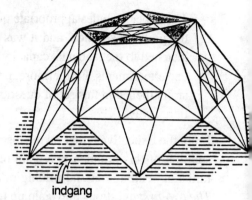

The owner of a camping ground wishes to get the swimming pool roofed.

The figure shows a sketch of the superstructure he wants to use.

On the figure sheet you can see an unfolding of the superstructure in scale 1:200.

indgang

- Construct the model as shown on the figure sheet.

The superstructure has to fulfil the following demands:

    a) a height of between 11 meters and 14 meters,

    b) an entrance at least 3 meters high,

    c) the whole pool should be roofed.

- *Investigate, whether the demands a), b) and c) are fulfilled, and state your arguments.*

- *Draw lines in the 5-gon onto the answer sheet, so that you get the same pattern as in the 5-gons on the superstructure.*

- *How many m^2 is the area of the horizontal part of the real roof?*

The five coloured triangles on the roof are made of glass.

- *How many m^2 is the glass area on the roof ?*

- *What percent (whole number) of the roof is glass?*

It is possible to show, that the glass part of the roof is exactly $5-2\sqrt{5}$

- *Calculate the value of this number to 2 decimal places.*

The assessment report continued:

    The degree of difficulty was great enough to challenge the abilities of every student, including the most efficient. Very few attained one hundred points, but also the less skilful students were given the chance of coping with several partial questions, which enabled everybody to gather more than just a few points.

The paper includes appropriate questions which call for creativity in the problem solution, and it was encouraging to see the importance attached to the students' capacity for explaining their considerations and experiments. Furthermore, it was noticed that geometry has been strengthened in this set of questions even in an amusing and untraditional way.

From the Executive Order on the distribution of points it appears that the solution of this problem may gain up to a maximum of 23 points. The initiating, cutting out and folding of the figure did not give any points. *The two first* questions may gain up to a maximum of 10 points, and it is up to the person in charge of the marking to decide on how to distribute those 10 points. Kirsten Haastrup chose to distribute the points so as to give a maximum of 6 points for the first question (with 2 points for a, 2 points for b, and 2 points for c), and 4 points for the second question.

Every year a number of meetings are held for teachers who are involved in the assessment and marking procedures, when the issue of distribution of points is discussed. On such occasions a debate often arises on the subject of the actual set of problems, whether for instance the subject is equally accessible for all students, including those living in urban areas, or in villages, boys and girls, etc. Moreover, the form of the individual test questions is discussed, and eventually the exchange of views at such meetings may result in an application to the committee on the selection of examination papers; this procedure keeps every examiner in touch with colleagues throughout the country.

The assessment report continued as follows:

Many external examiners consider the concrete activities in task no.6 involving cutting, folding, measuring, and calculations to be time-consuming, and they estimate the quantity of work to be larger than in previous years, but perhaps right for the greater part, too. Practically everybody managed to get started on the last question, but far from all succeeded in accomplishing the final area calculations and comparisons. The solid but slow calculator who answers each and every question has certainly had plenty to do.

With regard to the written grounds in the form of mathematical expressions and explanations of applied procedures a number of external examiners have noted a positive trend of developments. It is evident that coping in one way or another has become part of how students deal with this subject, though of course you may also come across classes or groups of students who seem to be concentrating primarily on attaining basic skills.

Every question is assessed, and the answers of the students to each question are assessed statistically. These assessments do not include a distribution by sex.

There is no collection of data on the answers by students to complete sets of questions or on marks. Distribution by sex is therefore not possible to determine.

During the last twenty years the objectives of education have undergone tremendous development, which is mirrored by innovations in examination papers. The intention has been to add new strength to those aspects of mathematics involving experience, experiments, discussions, and evaluation. By way of example, the requirements of education in statistics are that the students themselves collect information and data, deal with the material, discuss results, and reach conclusions.

It is difficult to work out written examination papers which test objectives of this kind. The objectives have brought about examination questions like the following set for students in grade 9:

Who did best in the tournament? Give reasons for your answer.

Find out if it was profitable to exchange into DM in Germany.

Find out if the demands were met and give reasons for your answer.

Find a formula for ....

and grade 10:

State which of the two equations describes the examination in the best way, and give reasons for your answer.

Determine the vertex of the parabola. What does the vertex tell you about the oak forest?

State formulae, expressed by radius r, for ....

31

In 1991, the following three problems among others were contained in 'The Advanced Final Examination':

Statistics

In September 'Seelandia' can offer room for 9900 overnight stays if all facilities are booked.

In April 29% are booked.
That means that the number of overnight stays is 29% of full capacity.

Måned:	jan	feb	mar	apr	maj	jun	jul	aug	sep	okt	nov	dec
Belægnings-procent:	24	48	41	29	42	53	97	82	39	54	28	33
Procentvis fordeling på nationaliteter:												
Danskere	53	45	42	47	47	43	36	17	49	60	44	34
Svenskere	6	28	19	25	13	29	33	14	17	14	32	19
Tyskere	40	27	39	28	38	28	29	68	34	25	23	47
Andre nationaliteter	1	0	0	0	2	0	2	1	0	1	1	0
I alt i %	100	100	100	100	100	100	100	100	100	100	100	100

How many overnight stays had 'Seelandia' in September ?

- *How many of those were Swedish people ?*

- *Explain, why 43% Danish overnight stays in June are more than 49% Danish overnight stays in September.*

In this problem a few statistical tables are included in order to test the student's ability to interpret this kind of material. To achieve a maximum of points for the last question starting with 'explain' the student has to give a wide description involving arithmetic terms.

Fountain

A fountain consists of a jet of water at its edge splashing into a large basin.

The jet of water forms part of a parabola curve.

At a certain water pressure the parabola curve can be described approximately by the equation:

$$y = -0.02x^2 + 200$$

- *Draw the parabola in a co-ordinate system using the scale of 1 cm corresponding to 20 cm.*

- *What distance from the edge of the basin at A does the jet hit the water surface ?*

With a different water pressure the parabola curve is determined by

$$y = -0.005x^2 + 200$$

- *Calculate the distance from the edge of the basin at A to the place where this jet hits the water surface.*

In this problem the function of the second degree is used as a means of describing the movement of a water jet. Students are tested to see if they are able to draw a parabola and to interpret it in the solution of a practical problem.

Decoration

In 'Seelandia' the end surface of a house is to be decorated. You wish to use a system of regularly filling out the surface, as shown on the picture at the bottom of this page.

Figur 1

The fundamental pattern for the picture is shown in figure 1.

- *Calculate the length of AM*

- *Draw on the answer sheet the second tier in the fundamental pattern.*

- *Complete the table on the answer sheet.*

The first tier in the picture below contains 6 animals.

- How many animals are in the third tier in the picture ?

34

In this problem art by Escher serves as a means to approach such different items as the theorem of Pythagoras, scale, power, and combinatorial analysis. This kind of problem appeals more or less to the skills of every student, although it also includes challenges to the most skilful among students — not least in the case of negative exponents.

To a greater extent the oral examination at the end of grade 10 reflects education from day to day because the questions may require activities involving experiments and examinations in the preparatory phase. As an example, dice may be used as an introduction to the presentation and discussion.

The rules of marking are the same as before, but in most cases teacher and examiner will discuss and reach an agreement; if not, the school principal is consulted. The student is given one mark.

It is the Ministry of Education's stated intention to push mathematics teaching towards mathematics used in real settings: In the 1991 examination paper of basic skills, one of the questions was the following: *'How much change do you get when you pay 20 kr. for 1 litre of ice-cream?'* Attached to the question is an advertisement showing a photo of 1 litre of ice- cream and the price of 15.85 kr. However, in 1988 a monetary reform was carried out in Denmark on which occasion the coins of 5-oere and 10-oere were abolished. The coin of 25 oere is now the lowest value. Therefore, in reality the answer to the question is 25 oere, whereas in the world of figures the correct answer would be 15 oere. However, in spite of objections from some teachers the Ministry of Education maintained that 15 oere was the correct answer — the numerical one.

Gender Issues

Research has been conducted into the effects of gender in primary and lower secondary school in general, for example in connection with the interaction between teacher and student. Furthermore, the effects of gender in physics/chemistry and in computer science classes have been the subject for research, but there has been no similar research into mathematics education. The problems which are associated with girls in relation to physics/chemistry are expected to derive from the late introduction of the subject in grade 7. Efforts are being made to introduce the subject in grade 3. It has been verified that when education in computer science starts late in puberty, the boys seize the computers, and the girls watch. However, it seems that this situation does not occur to the same degree when computers are used with younger pupils.

Our estimate of the relations between gender and mathematics education is therefore not based on proved research but on our knowledge of the discussions going on in the Association of Mathematics teachers, discussions in staff rooms, and on personal experience. Additionally our views are influenced by the debates which took place at the first Danish IOWME (International Organisation of Women and Mathematics Education), 1991.

In her capacity as external examiner Kirsten Haastrup has assessed about 400 Ordinary Final Examinations taken in 1992, and on the basis of the marks given she has compiled the gender differentiated data shown below. It is evident that the average mark of the girls is a little lower than that of the boys, and that the girls' results cluster towards marks of 8 and 9, whereas the boys are spread more widely over the marking scale. Average for boys is 8.55, average for girls is 8.26.

Marks for boys and for girls.

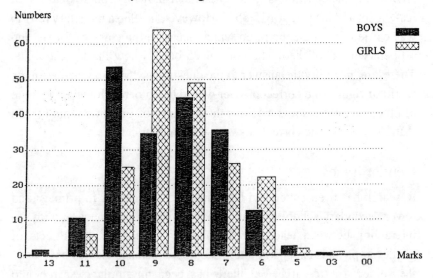

13 is the highest mark, 0 the lowest.

In our opinion the trend of developments over the last twenty years has proved beneficial to girls. The tendency is towards:

— broader aims with the intention of making mathematics feel more personal

— forms of education which allow students to bring forward their own ideas and proposals with respect to the scope and content of education

— experimental teaching styles (starting in the 1st grade where students may, for example, measure and weigh, cut and glue)

— students seeking outside contacts to get information

— the view of mathematics in a vital and practical context

— regarding mathematics no longer as a one-person subject where the calculations are made individually. In more recent sets of textbooks for example many questions have the wording: 'Form groups and discuss ...' and 'Make your assessment on the grounds of ...'.

— more geometry, which requires looking for patterns, etc. from the beginning, which may have the effect on students that they find it natural to use a method of examining things.

— replacing marks in the form of figures by broader assessments of how the individual student is improving her/his achievement. By this policy the risk is minimised of stamping somebody as untalented.

Teachers may choose their own methods. The individual teacher may buy, within financial limits, the books needed and makes decisions jointly with the students about the planning and accomplishment of education.

However, despite recent moves towards education which encourages female students, and despite a great many new and useful textbooks, much education still seems to persist in a formalised training in solving mathematical questions, rather than as a tool for thought and reflection. The higher the class level the stronger the tendency. There is obviously a large group of teachers who uses the exam as an excuse for defeating the purposes of the subject!

Also raising the question of gender has split teachers into two groups: One is of the opinion that if girls are profiting less than boys, the education and the teacher are to blame. The subject can and ought to offer pedagogic education which appeals to girls. The other group is of the opinion that girls are less talented in mathematics than boys, less involved, less committed, less interested, more conforming, more scared, etc., etc. If girls are achieving less than boys, it is genetic, primary socialisation, or the gendered roles in the labour market, whereas the school and teachers are not at fault.

For the moment, two topics in particular are discussed among teachers in primary and lower secondary schools:

a) As the students are not split, but kept together from the 1st to the 10th grade, we need to provide what we call 'differentiated teaching'. Differentiated teaching gives opportunity for the teacher to arrange different goals or different methods for groups of students or for individuals. This may in some cases apply to girls, if girls have certain interests or certain problems.

b) How to improve students' joint decision-taking and co responsibility.

Conclusion

We cannot prove in what way the subject makes equal room for both girls and boys. It is our impression, however, that the subject does not seem to cause serious problems for girls, and we are able to point to a number of trends of development which makes it plausible to practise a kind of education that appeals to girls and that this is used by many teachers.

Perhaps we are too naive. There is a risk that the gender problem may become serious without our noticing it. It came as a surprise when it was proved that both female and male teachers give more time to boy students than to girl students. And there may be other similar relationships of which we are not aware until the instances have been examined.

There remains a number of questions such as:

— what are the attitudes of the teachers to girls' and boys' skills for and interest in learning mathematics, and what effect does the approach have on their teaching and feedback to the students?

— how does education consider the needs and interests of girls and boys?

— how do the teachers distribute their attention between girls as well as boys?

— do the thematised sets of problem solutions have a discriminating effect because of the choice of context they have: some students are acquainted with it, others are not? Does sexual discrimination occur?

— how is it possible to improve the achievement of students in algebra as required by the Higher Education authorities without risking that education falls into grinding rules?

— how is it possible to maintain the creative dimension in education from the 1st through the 10th grades?

CHAPTER THREE

England and Wales

Marilyn Nickson
Stephanie Prestage

Introduction

Two major events have taken place in recent years within English and Welsh education. In 1986 a new single examination at 16+, the General Certificate of Secondary Education, was installed. In 1988 the Education Reform Act decreed that a National Curriculum was to be followed by all schools in the state sector in England and Wales. The combined effect of these events has been profound for mathematics education generally, but the implications for the mathematical education of girls have been particularly far reaching and important. We set out here to examine these effects and implications and to explore whether the result has been one of progress in redressing the imbalance that has existed in the past in the mathematical education of girls or whether it has been a case of 'two steps forward and three steps back'.

The developments have been at a fundamental level and it is impossible to grasp the effects of related assessment procedures on girls' mathematical education without first coming to terms with some of the structures that have evolved. In doing so, it is important to bear in mind that two main factors are particularly crucial with respect to gender issues. First, there are the effects of the three tier entry system for examination at 16+; second, is the important role played by coursework in assessing the performance of girls in particular. Each of these will be elaborated later. While the next few paragraphs may make little specific mention of gender, the intention is to trace how some developments have led to increased success in the mathematical achievement of girls at 16+ and how others more recently, seem poised to undermine that improved situation. However, as we shall see, the situation is not as clear cut as it may seem.

The Current Situation

The two major events referred to above have produced a new vocabulary for educationalists together with a plethora of acronyms to be remembered. In themselves they provide a very clear indication of the kind of thinking that underlies the government educational policy, characterised by linearity and compartmentalisation and representing a kind of supposed intellectual tidiness with no blurred edges. Some of these acronyms, after an initial interpretation, will be used within this chapter. The hierarchical conception is characteristic of the curriculum as a whole but is particularly so with respect to mathematics.

The General Certificate of Secondary Education

The new General Certificate of Secondary Education (GCSE) replaced the old two tier system at 16+, which comprised the General Certificate of Education (GCE), catering for the old grammar school (able, academic) candidate and offering subjects at Ordinary-level and Advanced-level, and the Certificate of Secondary Education (CSE) which was for the remaining candidates. Two of the fundamental objectives of the new GCSE in providing a single 16+ examination system were stated in a Department of Education and Science (DES) document as, 'to improve the quality of Education and to raise standards of attainment by stretching and stimulating pupils throughout the ability range' and 'to produce a system which is fair to candidates, both in the award of grades and in access to the examinations' (DES, 1984 pp.2-3). They went on to describe how the examination would be designed 'not for any particular proportion of the ability range, but for all candidates, whatever their ability relative to other candidates, who are able to reach the standards required for the award of particular grades in each subject'. (*ibid* p.3)

National Criteria and the National Curriculum

These standards were to be developed in relation to content that has been determined according to National Criteria. These have been identified for mathematics (as well as other subjects) within the National Curriculum and this content has been grouped according to five Attainment Targets (AT). These are: AT1 — Using and Applying Mathematics; AT 2 — Number; AT3 — Algebra; AT4 — Shape and Space; AT5 — Handling Data (Ed. note: The five are currently being reviewed to become four, it is rumoured). Linearity is emphasised further by the identification of Programmes of Study for individual AT's and ten levels of attainment within each. Finally, associated with each of these ten levels are Statements of Attainment (SoAs) which have taken on a special significance in the curricular structure since they have come (whether intentionally or not) to represent the criteria for the assessment of mathematics within the National Curriculum.

These criteria in the form of SoAs have achieved their status because they provide the link between the GCSE and the National Curriculum. Within the National Curriculum as a whole, four Key Stages have been identified at which students are to be assessed 'by a combination of standard national tests and teachers' own assessment' (DES, 1991 pp.5-6). Key Stage Three is at 14+ years of age and following it, a two-year course leads to assessment at Key Stage 4 when students of 16+ are assessed. (The first such examination took place in 1994 so that from September 1992 mathematics curricula had to be geared to the relevant assessment procedures but attempts to relate assessment to the ten levels within the Attainment Targets are currently in abeyance. Thus the intended meeting point of the GCSE and the National Curriculum has yet to be fully established.)

Differentiation by tiers of entry and kinds of assessment

The intention of the GCSE since its inception has been to award grades related to specific criteria and to assess positive achievement, thus attempting to assess what students know, understand, and can do, as opposed to identifying what they cannot. It represents a move away from norm-referenced to criterion-referenced assessment. In order to achieve this, a differentiated approach to assessment was adopted which, in mathematics, has taken the form of identifying three tiers of examination referred to as the Foundation, Intermediate, and Higher tiers, one of the important features that has had particular repercussions for girls, as we shall see later. Differentiation in assessment of mathematics was one of the recommendations of the Cockcroft Report (DES, 1982) where the view adopted was that not all students should be expected to succeed at all of the mathematics curriculum but that the curriculum should be generated from the 'bottom upwards' as opposed to from the 'top down'. The Cockcroft report also recognised that not all mathematics was best assessed by written examinations and advocated a proportion of teacher-assessed work within the curriculum. This too was adopted within the GCSE and by 1991, at least 20% of the examination of all mathematics curricula was represented by teacher-assessed work or what has now come to be known as 'coursework'. This, again, has become an extremely important factor in relation to the assessment of the performance of girls in mathematics.

Before considering how these developments specifically relate to gender issues within mathematics education in the UK, however, we shall first review the recent literature related to these issues.

Recent Thought on Gender Issues in Mathematics Education in the UK

In the past 10 years several publications in the United Kingdom have provided information and comment relevant to gender issues in learning mathematics. There have also been a variety of initiatives designed to investigate the situation and to promote awareness of the facts.

The first major report from an enquiry into the teaching of mathematics in schools was the Cockcroft Report (DES, 1982), referred to above, which included an appendix on the differences in mathematical performance between girls and boys. Drawing on historical, statistical and research evidence, it confirmed that by the age of sixteen boys gained a significantly higher proportion of A-C grades in the old Ordinary Level GCE (the precursor of the GCSE) and a far larger proportion of boys went on to do Advanced level mathematics. Unbiased books and equipment and good careers advice were suggested for removing the imbalance in performance at the higher end of the ability range. Also suggested was the need to heighten teachers' expectations of girls to 'tackle higher cognitive level tasks and not be content with success at low level tasks such as routine computation.' (DES, 1982, para B36).

Walden and Walkerdine (1982, 1985) offered the reminder that not all girls are bad at mathematics and that in fact there is very little difference between girls' and boys' performance. They then added a further dimension to the arguments put forward for differential achievement, criticising the interpretations placed by teachers upon girls' achievements. They claimed that girls are not out-performed by boys, but girls' successes are interpreted differently (reflected by the author of the Cockcroft appendix (op cit) with comments on the girls' successes in 'low level tasks' and 'routine computation'.) The achievements of the girls were more likely to be put down to rule — following rather than real understanding. They stated that:

> Examining the relationship between the ideas about the teaching and learning of mathematics and classroom practices produced a reading of success and failure in which actual attainment is no longer a simple or reliable indicator of success. The move towards 'real understanding' and away from 'rote memorisation' means that certain characteristics are invested in the individual. It is therefore possible to be successful for the wrong reasons. That is a child may do well but be suspected of 'not understanding'. (1985: 143).

Indicators of 'real understanding' say the authors, are to a large extent similar to those used to describe masculinity, such as challenging, questioning and breaking rules. They hypothesise further that there is therefore a problem for many girls in that the characteristics of femininity which they display lead teachers to assume a lack of understanding.

Practical implications

A teaching pack called *Girls into Mathematics* incorporated many activities for mathematics departments to use as a focus for action and discussion to help girls to achieve their potential in the mathematics classroom. In the companion volume to this pack, (*Girls into Maths Can Go*, Burton, 1986), Rosalinde Scott-Hodgetts built upon some of the arguments forwarded by Walden and Walkerdine (1985), that is that some girls are disadvantaged in mathematics at the end of their primary schooling by virtue of their success. However her interpretation of the situation was that the disadvantage is not solely the result of affective factors which encourage them to concentrate their efforts on particular areas of the curriculum. She suggested that some pupils may be adhering to a set of strategies which have led to their success in mathematics but which, when used exclusively, have negative implications for their mathematical development.

Rosalinde Scott-Hodgetts' (1986) argument is built upon the work of Gordon Pask who established a strong case for the existence of two distinct learning styles — serialistic and holistic. She interpreted these in the following way:

> Serialists proceed from certainty to certainty, learning, remembering and recapitulating a body of information in small, well-defined and sequentially ordered 'parcels'. They may appreciate topics ahead of those they understand, but they tend not to look far ahead; they are cautious, 'one step at a time' learners who are confident that the necessary knowledge will be gained steadily. Holists, on the other hand, prefer to start in an exploratory way, working first towards an understanding of an overall framework, and then filling in the details; they will tend to speculate about relationships during the learning process and will in general remember and recall bodies of knowledge in terms of 'higher order relations'. (p. 68)

Early learning of mathematics often focuses on algorithmic methods for computation in which girls appear to be successful (APU, 1982). Such algorithmic strategies are often serialistic in style. As mathematics becomes more complex, suggested Rosalinde Scott-Hodgetts, so a combination of serialistic and holistic skills is desirable. What is needed to be successful in mathematics isto be a versatile learner.

> It is the belief of the writer that children who are predisposed to a serialistic approach are less likely to develop into versatile learners within the mathematics classroom than those who are inclined to adopt holistic strategies; this situation is held to be directly attributable to teacher behaviour. (Scott-Hodgetts, 1986. p. 70)

In 1986 the Royal Society, in conjunction with the Institute of Mathematics and its Applications published *Girls and Mathematics* (1986). Similar to the Cockcroft report (DES, 1982) this contains statistical information, some comment on relevant research and a chapter on recommendations to the various sections involved in mathematics education. It reiterated the advice to be found in Cockcroft and advised the use of *Girls into Mathematics* as a bench mark for practice. It further highlighted the need for discussion in the mathematics classroom.

> Encourage all pupils to talk about mathematics... Introduce group work and co-operative teaching styles; do not allow boys to dominate discussion in mixed groups or girls to defer to boys in discussion. (p.4)

The role of discussion in the mathematics classroom and its importance for all learners was further emphasised in an APU report (APU, 1988) and HMI report (DES, 1989).

Assessment issues

In the build-up to the construction and description of a National Curriculum and National Assessments at the ages of 7, 11, 14 and 16 in England and Wales, a greater emphasis on assessment issues drew together the research on aspects of test design and differential achievement in certain areas. In the submission to the Task Group on Assessment and Testing (TGAT) on behalf of the Equal Opportunities Commission, Harvey Goldstein summarised the evidence for gender differences (DES, F, 1987) under the headings: reading, writing, test format and motivation and context. The report warned of possible differential achievement between boys and girls:

> As with most assessments the results of the standard assessment are likely to show differences between groups. It is possible that there will be sex differences in some attainment areas; for example on average, girls score more highly than boys in certain writing tasks. Generally though, the position is not so simple — in mathematics boys do better in some topic areas and girls in others. There is also some evidence that different types of test favour one or other group (e.g. boys may do better in multiple choice tests). (DES, 1987 para 51)

The final report *Mathematics for ages 5-16* (DES, 1988) by the National Curriculum mathematics working group included a short section on equal opportunities. This suggested a wide variety of modes of assessment should be used and that teaching materials and examples should be free from gender bias.

Stobart et al (1991) took one further step in considering the use of assessment to bring males and females 'into line' (p.2). They took up the challenge that Harvey Goldstein offered, which they admitted was a provocative alternative:

> If we... wished to have an exam which produced equal score or grade distributions for boys and girls, then we might be able to achieve this by careful choice of question format, content etc. There are, of course, considerable difficulties in the way of achieving such an end, one being that entry rates for different exams differ markedly. Nevertheless, the resulting examinations might do much to encourage the sexes to participate more equally in certain subjects and the resulting effects on teaching and curriculum would be a rather interesting example of an assessment led pedagogy. (1986 pp. 3-4)

Controlling the structure of examinations to allow for equal outcome (rather than for equal opportunity) raises many questions. If, as the APU (1988) reported, girls do better on computation, probability and algebra and boys do better on volume and geometry, what might be the balance of topics in an examination to encourage a more equal outcome? If gender difference in performance is to be treated as a consequence of test items rather than 'indicative of a particular view of educational achievement' (Stobart et al, 1991 p. 3), is equality of opportunity in the learning of mathematics assumed to be happening in all mathematics classrooms? As Patrick (1990) suggests in this respect, GCSE may be 'perpetuating features of previous examinations which it may not be desirable to perpetuate'. (p. 3). If future examinations are to focus very specifically on Statements of Attainment as identified in the National Curriculum, an analysis of these in terms of girl/boy mathematical strengths could suggest that one or the other will be disadvantaged and equality of opportunity will be more elusive.

A brief analysis of the various models of GCSE examinations in mathematics should help develop a clearer picture of the situation as it exists at the moment.

The GCSE Examination System

The two new features introduced in the GCSE examination system (and referred to earlier) are the differentiation into three tiers (Foundation, Intermediate and Higher) and the introduction of coursework as a feature of the assessment procedures. In this section we shall look first of all at the relationships between the achievement of girls and (a) the tier of entry and (b) the various examination systems that have been adopted with their different proportions of coursework.

Tiers of entry

As already noted, the DES set out to establish through the GCSE an examination system which was to be fair to candidates in the grades awarded and in access to examinations. The idea of three tiers for teaching and assessing mathematics as suggested by Cockcroft (DES, 1982) was duly adopted. The grades of the new GCSE examination replacing the old GCE examination system were developed from a direct combination of the GCE and CSE grades as shown below (where U signifies Ungraded).

GCE	A	B	C	D	E			
CSE			1	2	3	4	5	U
GCSE	A	B	C	D	E	F	G	

Following this, restricted grade ranges were identified with each tier as follows:

Higher	A	B	C	D	U		
Intermediate			C	D	E	F	U
Foundation				E	F	G	U

As this suggests, the highest grade available to an Intermediate tier candidate is a C and to a Foundation candidate, an E. This form of awarding grades has had wide repercussions (not all of which will be discussed here) but what is of particular relevance to the performance of girls in mathematics is the tier at which they are entered. Table 1 below

Table 1: GCSE Mathematics Entry Patterns (1988-90)						
Tier	1988		1989		1990	
	Male	Female	Male	Female	Male	Female
Foundation (E-G) % of total	48.0	52.0	47.8	52.2	48.4	51.6
Intermediate (C-F) % of total	47.0	53.0	46.1	53.9	45.7	54.3
Higher (A-C) % of total	52.8	47.2	53.2	45.8	52.4	47.6
Total Entry	320863	335576	301580	321179	241346	260865
% of total	48.9	51.1	48.4	51.6	48.1	51.9

taken from Stobart et al (1991) shows a breakdown of the pattern of entry according to gender in the different tiers.

The table shows clearly that although there are more girls (51.9% of the total) than boys (48.1% of the total) entered for GCSE by 1990, 52.4% of entries at the Higher tier are boys. More girls, proportionally, are entered at the Intermediate and Foundation tiers. Research currently being carried out shows that decisions made with respect to entry to tier are made most often by teaching staff alone and it is therefore teachers' perceptions of candidates' ability that is the overriding factor in making these decisions. The fact that fewer girls are entered at the Higher tier suggests that teachers are, at best, 'playing safe' in their judgements about girls' mathematical ability. There is also evidence from this research that teachers perceive girls as not coping well in the examination situation and that by entering them at the Intermediate tier, some of the assumed strain of assessment might be alleviated.

Table 2: Number of candidates achieving A, B and C grades in GCSE Mathematics from all syllabuses, Summer 1990.			
Grade	A	B	C
Male	27812 (8.6)*	33295 (10.3)	77336 (24.0)
Female	19784 (5.8)	28686 (8.4)	80261 (23.5)
Total	47601 (7.2)**	61983 (9.3)	157606 (23.7)
* Proportion (%) of entries for the gender category achieving the grade			
** Proportion (%) of total entry achieving the grade			
Source: IGRC Statistics Summer 1990.			

The results of examinations for 1990 provide more detail about the achievement of girls and boys in terms of grades awarded.

This shows clearly that more girls than boys achieve a C grade although this is a smaller proportion of the total number of female candidates compared to that of male candidates. The question arises as to how many of those might have achieved an A or a B (or indeed a C) had they been entered in the Higher tier. There is every possibility that this could have been the case since current research shows that the work of candidates at the very top of the Intermediate tier is comparable with that of Higher tier candidates and has been judged to be worthy of a higher grade. At the same time, a large majority of schools responding to a questionnaire identified the fact that in their opinion, in retrospect there were pupils who could have achieved a higher grade had they been placed in a higher tier. Finally this research also shows that rather than differentiating in terms of what mathematics is taught and how, to most students at GCSE level, differentiation in most schools is, in fact, limited to assessment only and the level of examination at which pupils are entered. Taking all of these factors into consideration suggests that the effects of differentiation on the achievement of girls in mathematics are very complex and not necessarily advantageous.

The research of Licht and Dweck (1983) is relevant here. They reported that children's beliefs about the cause of their own failure or lack of achievement generally are not just *predictors* but also *causes* of what they call achievement behaviours, and that failure linked to lack of ability has a greater negative effect than any other on further performance. Girls in particular are inclined to see failure as an indication of their ability (or lack of it) as opposed to any other factors (e.g. the way they have been taught or their own lack of effort). Thus any failure in mathematics brings about a self-perpetuating situation with respect to their achievement in the subject and they come to believe in their lack of ability to do mathematics. A further complication in this already complex situation is the reported tendency on the part of girls to want to avoid success in mathematics. Keeves(1988) reported that 'this attitude acts more strongly towards more quantitative studies, perceived to be a male preserve, than towards verbal and language studies.' (p. 486) Added to this is the visibility of success or failure with respect to learning mathematics (Nickson, 1992) and the fact that such visibility is likely to be more disadvantageous for girls than it is for boys (Licht and Dweck, 1983).

These factors that result from experience built up over time, together with the development of self-perceptions that accompany them, must affect girls' attitudes towards mathematics. The question that arises is the degree of teachers' awareness of these factors and their effects on girls' attitudes when they select them for entry into tiers for the GCSE examination. Any apparent lack of confidence or willingness on the part of girls (as perceived by their teachers) may be due to one or other or indeed all of these factors and possibly others.

GCSE — Variations on a theme

The differentiation introduced in the GCSE has resulted in the five examination boards of England and Wales offering different approaches

Diagram A: Presentation of end-of-course examination papers

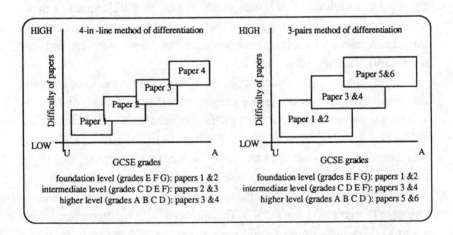

to the presentation of examination papers. They are presented either as a 4-in-line method where adjacent tiers have a common paper (also known as the 'chain model') or a 3- pairs model where there are common questions in papers between adjacent tiers (known as 'parallel papers') shown below (Diagram A).

Coursework was not a compulsory part of the GCSE examination until 1991, as already noted.

Table 3: Grades in O'level and CSE, 1987, and GCSE mathematics, 1988 and 1991

| | Percentage of candidates gaining grade | | | | | | |
	A	B	C/1	D/2	E/3	F/4	G/5
GCE/CSE 1987	7	11	19	12	16	17	10
GCSE 1988	6	9	22	16	16	15	7
GCSE 1991	9	9	26	16	17	13	6
The percentage are given to the nearest whole number							
Source: HMI (1989) & AEB (1991)							

By 1987 about 37% of candidates gained a grade C or above. In 1988, the new examination results showed a similar picture but there was a significant increase by 1991 as seen in Table 3 below.

It is interesting to speculate what the 1991 figures might represent, beyond those already considered above in relation to girls and tier of entry. Writers differ on interpretation, ranging from an increase in standards to a lowering of examination demands or to a manipulation of statistics. Nevertheless, a look at the detailed comparison of the GCSE grades obtained by boys and girls in 1988 and 1991 (Table 4 below) shows a continuing situation of a smaller percentage of girls attaining the higher grades. 40.2% of boys gained a grade C or better compared with 33.1% of girls in 1988, and 45.9% compared with 41.7% respectively, in 1991.

All of the examination boards offered (at this time) many different course options in mathematics syllabuses at 16+. It was possible for a mathematics department to choose an examination for their pupils that

Table 4: Grades on O'level and CSE, 1987, and GCSE mathematics, 1988 & 1991

| | Percntage of candidates gaining grade | | | | | | |
1988	A	B	C	D	R	F	G
Girls	4.8	7.7	20.6	16.4	16.3	16.4	7.8
Boys	7.4	9.6	23.2	15.4	16.4	14.2	6.2
1991							
Girls	7.7	8.6	25.4	16.7	17.8	13.2	6.1
Boys	10.2	9.8	25.9	15.5	16.7	12.2	5.7
Source: HMI (1989) & AEB (1991)							

Table 5

	Final examination	Coursework	Oral
Option 1(67,896)	80%	15%	5%
Option 2 (13,456)	66%	28%	5%
Option 3 (9,796)	50%	50% modular assessment	
Option 4 (7,470)	50%	45%	5%
Option 5 (1,443)		100% continual assessment	

reflected the department's own philosophy about the teaching and learning of mathematics. For example, there was an examination based on an individualised learning scheme with 50% continual assessment (i.e. coursework) and 50% end of course examination. Alternatively, it was also possible to choose a graded assessment scheme with 100% continual assessment or a more traditional syllabus with the major focus being on the end of course examination (SEAC decreed more recently that no mathematics syllabus may be assessed by a coursework component worth more than 20% of the total course marks). Even the way that coursework was, and still is, assessed is open to department preference from tasks set by the examination board done in school time under supervision with a time limit of one hour, to free selection of open-ended tasks to be done in the candidate's own time as extended pieces of work. As a consequence the data available for analysis, though rich and varied, makes comparison difficult.

Goulding (1992) analysed the statistics from four options in mathematics from a single examination board. She selected four syllabuses which attracted the largest numbers, two of which are associated with commercially published mathematics schemes. There are significant differences between the weighting of assessment components in the four options which reflect the variations to be found among the examination syllabuses offered by all the boards. Added to her data for further comparison is a fifth option offered by the same board, based on a graded assessment scheme. Table 5 shows the structure of the assessment scheme for each. In their research carried out prior to the introduction of the GCSE, Walden and Walkerdine (1985) found that more girls were being entered for the easier Certificate of Secondary Education examinations with restricted grades, compared with the GCE 'O' level examination. Goulding (1992) suggested that

> This may have been done with benevolent intentions in an attempt to shield girls from pressure, but none the less reduced their chances of performing on equal terms and no doubt compounded the problems of low expectations. (Goulding, 1992 p. 38)

This possibility has already been suggested here with respect to the entry of girls in the different tiers of the GCSE. However, a more detailed consideration of the current entry policy with respect to the GCSE shows how the pattern of entry related to different types of GCSE course.

Patterns of entry and coursework

Table 6 shows the outcomes of the examinations of the four options studied by Goulding (1992).

Table 6: Percentage of candidates entered in each of the options from Table 4					
	Foundation	Intermediate	Higher	Higher and Extension Paper	
Option 1					
Male	15.3	48	32.6	4	(32,237 sat)
Female	16.3	50.6	30.1	2.9	(35,659 sat)
Option 2					
Male	27	49	24		(6,589 sat)
Female	27.4	50.7	22		(6,867 sat)
Option 3					
Male	35.7	47.7	16.5		(4,845 sat)
Female	33.8	48.3	18		(4,949 sat)
Option 4					
Male	24.8	49.6	21.9	3.7	(3,625 sat)
Female	23.6	52.2	21.2	3	(3,845 sat)

Apart from Option 3 which carries a 50% modular coursework assessment, the percentage of girls entered for the Higher tier is smaller than that for boys. However, actual figures give a different picture where entry numbers show that more girls are being entered at the two lower tiers than at the Higher tier and for the Extension Paper in all the options except Option 2. The trend from the previous three years shows that in each of these years there were actually more boys in this age range than girls which, if the same holds true for 1991, suggests that the achievements of girls in the GCSE examination are even more marked. (The total number of male and female school leavers in 1991 is not yet available from the government's statistical services department.)

Table 7: Percentage of candidates gaining grades in each of the options from Table 4

Option 1	A	B	C	D	E	F	G	U
Male	14.6	14.5	25.4	17.5	12.4	9.3	3.7	2.7
Female	13.7	13.3	25.4	18.1	12.2	10.1	4.2	2.9

In this option, 55.4 per cent of male and 52.4 per cent of female candidates obtained grade C or higher.

Option 2								
Male	6.8	7	23.3	15.1	19.2	14.7	7.9	6
Female	5.2	6.3	21.4	16.5	20	16.5	8.2	5.9

37.1 per cent male, 32.9 per cent female with grade C or above

Option 3								
Male	5.5	4.6	18.2	15.4	15	23.3	14.2	3.7
Female	6.1	5.3	18.4	15.8	15.2	21.6	14.1	3.4

28.3 per cent male, 29.8 per cent female with grade C or above.

Option 4								
Male	8.2	11.7	26.1	18	19	11.1	5	1.5
Female	7.2	12.1	29.2	19	17.1	10	4.2	1.3

46 per cent of male, 48.5 per cent female with grade C or above

Option 5								
Male	6.5	8.6	18.4	16.2	11.0	13.9	21.9	3.5
Female	6.0	12.6	21.5	17.2	15.0	13.3	11.7	2.6

33.5 per cent male, 40.1 per cent female with grade C or above.

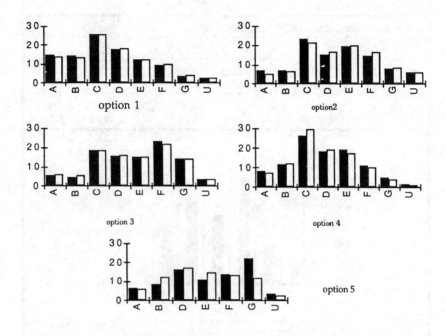

Table 7 gives the distribution of the grades of each of the five options referred to earlier and is followed by a graphical representation of the data (Diagrams B, C, D E and F). They show a similar picture to that in Table 6 relating to entry tier, with proportionally fewer girls gaining higher grades while actual numbers show minimal differences.

It would seem that Options 3,4 and 5 (with the higher proportions of coursework) offer the girls a better opportunity for success in terms of higher grades though, as Goulding (1992) pointed out, a causal relationship would be difficult to justify on the evidence to hand due to the variations in the examination structures and the significant differences in grade distributions. Added support to the coursework-is-better argument are the statistics from another examination board that offers end of course examination with either 20% or 40% coursework. Both proportionally and in actual numbers, the girls attained better in the 40% coursework across the higher grades that in the 20% coursework option.

In addition to the evidence from current research reported above, there is also a wealth of anecdotal evidence that girls are producing better coursework assignments than boys. One head of mathematics department

Table 8: Attainment patterns in a GCSE 40% and 20% coursework option

40% course option, males = 16,970; females = 19,535.

	A	B	C	D	E	F	G	U
Male	856	1730	4495	2825	3449	2231	806	578
	5.0	10.2	26.5	16.6	20.3	13.1	4.7	3.4
Female	979	2072	5639	3235	3837	2306	860	571
	5.0	10.6	28.9	16.5	16.8	11.8	4.4	2.9

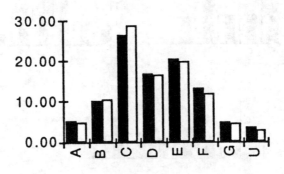

20% coursework option, males = 20,856; females 22,329

	A	B	C	D	E	F	G	U
Male	1317	1926	5423	4001	4138	2263	926	859
	6.3	9.2	26.0	19.2	19.8	10.9	4.4	4.1
Female	1086	1805	6329	4498	4155	2535	882	1038
	4.7	8.1	28.3	20.1	18.6	11.4	5.9	4.6

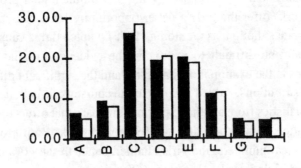

also reports an increase in confidence that GCSE assessment styles have produced in her students:

> They speak of their earlier fear of mathematics and of how GCSE coursework helped them to overcome this fear and to realise that they did have ability in mathematics. (Ball, 1992 p. 39)

Coursework — The Nature of its Importance for Girls Learning Mathematics

It should be heartening that the gap between boys and girls in measured achievement with respect to mathematics is closing as a result of the introduction of coursework. While this may be the case, however, it is wrong to be lulled into the belief that coursework in itself can or will bring about equal opportunity for girls in learning mathematics. Firstly, what has to be borne in mind is the recent decision that, in future, there will be a maximum of 20% coursework for any mathematics syllabus and that syllabuses without coursework will be available for any school department that wishes to adopt one. Thus any success gained by girls as a result of the coursework element of their mathematical studies may be lost where the decision is taken by a school to adopt a syllabus without such an element. Perhaps more important, however, are the more subtle reasons associated with general perceptions of coursework that are at play in the teaching and learning situation taken together with research about girls' academic achievement generally.

Views of coursework

There has been difficulty in the past in identifying an agreed perception of what constitutes coursework. Kingdom and Stobart (1988) stated simply that coursework is 'defined as any teacher assessed component'. (p. 72) An even more succinct definition was offered by Macintosh (1986) when he said that 'Very simply it is work undertaken during a course.' (p. 22). However, if we were to search for a prescribed or 'official' view of what constitutes coursework, it must be advisable to accept that offered in the most recent edition of the criteria for GCSE mathematics as published by the Secondary Examinations and Assessment Council in March 1992. In the glossary of terms, the entry under coursework is as follows:

Coursework consists of in-course tasks set and undertaken according to conditions prescribed by an awarding body. Coursework tasks are integral to rather than incidental to the course of study. Coursework is marked by a candidate's own teacher according to criteria provided and exemplified by the awarding body — taking national requirements into account. It is moderated by the awarding body. (no page)

The criteria in both of the previous definitions are included within this (it is teacher assessed and undertaken during a course) but it goes beyond these in involving external agencies, i.e. the awarding body (the examining board) and the government (in the guise of the National Curriculum). Thus whatever form coursework takes for the GCSE, it is moderated by an external body and satisfies the National Criteria for mathematics. It would appear, therefore, to have become more public and to have achieved some status as a result of its 'official' adoption within the GCSE as a whole. However, it is important to appreciate the historical status of coursework to understand its particular significance in relation to the assessment of girls' performance in mathematics.

Historical perspectives

Macintosh (1986) pointed out that coursework has been with us for a very long time in public examinations but long-standing attitudes 'have caused it to fall foul of the British obsession for preferring to do worse on those examinations which carry greater prestige rather than to do better on those that are more useful.' (Macintosh, 1986 p. 22) The tendency is to view coursework as 'all right for the less able' (ibid). This commonly held perception of this form of assessment in itself may damage its status but together with the research evidence related to girls learning mathematics, the effect becomes really serious.

We have seen that research on gender issues in educational achievement has shown that girls tend to judge failure in terms of ability (Licht and Dweck, 1983, Keeves, 1988). There is also the evidence from Walden and Walkerdine (1986) referred to earlier which indicated the possibility of being 'successful for the wrong reasons'. (p.143). The suggestion is that teachers do not value the success of girls for the right reasons and tend not to give credit for 'real understanding'. It seems likely, in view of the traditionally held view of coursework, that it would not be taken by all teachers as an indicator of this 'real understanding'. Similarly it might not be considered to provide evidence of the higher cognitive level tasks referred to by Cockcroft (DES, 1982).

Research related to perceptions of coursework

Before considering specific mathematical implications, it is important to note other more recent factors that reinforce these views of coursework. One of these relates to the fact that coursework in mathematics became compulsory for all GCSE courses to be examined in 1991 which meant that relevant syllabuses would have to be adopted by September 1989. Figures related to one syllabus alone show that in spite of this, in the 1990 examination, 42,061 candidates were entered in 1988 for a mathematics examination without coursework (MEG Mathematics Syllabus 1650) while only 20,174 candidates were entered for the comparable syllabus with coursework (MEG Mathematics Syllabus 1651). (AEB, 1990) This indicates that a very large proportion of schools following this syllabus held out as long as possible before adopting a version of it that included coursework. While this in itself may not provide conclusive evidence of attitudes on the part of mathematics teachers towards coursework, it does at the very least suggest that there was some reluctance to adopt it in many schools and that this reluctance may in part have been due to perceptions of its status and its relevance to the subject of mathematics.

A second factor in this respect is the recent decision on the part of the government to rescind a previous decision that all GCSE syllabuses in all subjects must include an element of coursework. In its stead, the decision has been taken that syllabuses either may have no coursework at all or the amount permitted will be limited, and that while this limit may be 30% in the case of science or higher in other subjects, it must not exceed 20% in mathematics. This seems to be a very specific message that this mode of work and assessment is not considered to be particularly valued in the case of mathematics but that it is more appropriate to other areas of the curriculum. Once again then, the status of coursework within the mathematics curriculum has been undermined and its value implicitly questioned.

Implications for assessing girls' mathematical achievement at 16+.

All of this suggests that the traditional views about coursework referred to above are still held by many directly involved in the teaching and assessment of mathematics as well as by those who are decision makers at governmental level. It seems likely that given this lack of external support for coursework, the hesitancy of teachers themselves to adopt it in mathematics would be reinforced. This may be because they do not see it as an indicator of the 'real understanding' of mathematics mentioned earlier and that while girls may be achieving a higher level of performance in coursework, they are not judged by teachers to be gaining this success in mathematics for the 'right reasons'. Their success may be attributed to standard of presentation and degree of perseverance as opposed to the quality of their mathematical understanding. This is borne out by the current study exploring the decision making policies of schools in entering pupils at different tiers. In response to a question asking who benefited most from coursework, the second most frequent response was 'girls' and most often with a comment that either they were careful about organisation and presentation or that they disliked the written examination situation. There was no suggestion that teachers considered that better performance in coursework was related to girls showing a deeper understanding of the mathematics involved.

The evidence provided by the Cockcroft report (DES, 1982) is also relevant here. Their plea (reported above) that teachers' expectations of girls must be heightened in relation to their ability to tackle higher level cognitive tasks in order to overcome the disparities between them and boys may not be seen to be addressed in the process of doing coursework. For example, a piece of work entitled 'Costing a Holiday' or 'Geometry in Nature' (MEG Mathematics Syllabus 1651, 1990) might not be construed by teachers as being of appropriate mathematical rigour when compared with questions on pure algebra or geometry. If this is indeed the case and a proportion of teachers choose syllabuses without an element of coursework, a second Cockcroft (DES,1982) recommendation, namely that there should be a variety of forms of assessing mathematical learning, will not be fulfilled.

Conclusion

Assessment in mathematics at 16+ in the UK today has very specific messages with respect to equal opportunities for girls studying the subject. First, it is clear that in attempting to instigate a system which is fair to candidates as intended, the differentiation model for the assessment of the GCSE has resulted in curtailing the potential of girls for achieving at higher levels in mathematics and in reinforcing not only girls' own perceptions of their low mathematical ability but those of their teachers as well. Teachers' perceptions of girls in the context of assessing mathematics are such in wishing to avoid pressurising girls and making them over-anxious by placing them in lower tiers of examination entry, they have limited their horizons considerably. Second, while coursework as a form of assessment has given us strong indications about the ways in which girls can perform well mathematically, long held perceptions of the value of coursework in mathematics may harden beliefs that girls cannot do 'proper' mathematics well and are succeeding as a result of taking an easier option rather than achieving at a higher cognitive level.

Rather than producing a fair system for all, the differentiation model for GCSE mathematics together with related assessment procedures, appear to be doing just the opposite. They are reinforcing traditional beliefs about girls and mathematics rather than raising standards of attainment and producing a system which is fair in terms of access to examinations, as was intended. Until teachers' perceptions of girls' performance in mathematics is changed, as well as those of girls themselves, and until the value of the kinds of mathematical learning and assessment undertaken in coursework is fully recognised, the vicious circle that gives rise to unequal opportunities for girls will not be broken.

Acknowledgement

The authors would like to thank Jannette Elwood for her help in supplying some of the statistical data that appears in this paper.

Bibliography

Associated Examining Board (1990) *Inter-Group Statistics Summer 1990*, Guildford, Surrey: AEB

Associated Examining Board (1991) *Inter-Group Statistics Summer 1991*, Guildford, Surrey: AEB

Assessment Performance Unit (1982) *A review of monitoring in mathematics 1978-1982* Part 1 & 2, Windsor: NFER-Nelson

Assessment Performance Unit (1988) *Attitudes and Gender Differences*, Windsor: NFER-Nelson

Ball, B. (1992) *Raising a Monster*, Times Educational Supplement February 21 1992

Burton, L. (ed) (1986) *Girls Into Maths Can Go*, Sussex: Holt Education

DES (1982) Mathematics Counts: *Report of the Committee of Inquiry into the Teaching of Mathematics in Schools*, (The Cockcroft Report) London: HMSO

DES (1985) *General Certificate of Secondary Education. A general introduction*, London: HMSO

DES (1987) *National Curriculum Task Group on Assessment and Testing*, London: HMSO

DES (1988) *National Curriculum Mathematics for Ages 5 to 16*, London: HMSO

DES (1989) Education Observed: Girls Learning Mathematics, London: HMSO

DES (1991) *The Education Reform Act — National Curriculum; Mathematics and Science Orders Under Section 4*, London: HMSO

DES (1992) *GSCE/Key Stage 4: Standard for Assessment and Certification*, London Schools Examinations and Assessment Council March 1992

Evaluation and Monitoring Unit (1991) *APU Mathematics Monitoring (Phase 2)*, London: Schools Examination and Assessment Council

Goldstein (1986) Gender bias and test norms in education selection, *Research Intelligence* 23 2-4

Goulding, M. (1992) *Lets hear it for the girls*, Times Educational Supplement February 21 1992

Keeves, J. P. (1988) Sex differences in ability and achievement in Keeves J. P. (ed) (1988) *Education Research, Methodology and Measurement: An International Handbook*, Oxford: Pergamon Press

Licht, B. G. and Dweck, C. S. (1988) Sex Differences in Achievement Orientations: Consequences for academic choices and attainments in Marland, M. (ed) *Sex Differences and Schooling*, London: Heineman

Kingdom, M. and Stobart, G. (1988) *GCSE Examined*, Sussex: The Falmer Press

Macintosh, H. (1986) The Sacred Cows of Coursework in the *GCSE: An Uncommon Examination*, Bedford Way Papers 29, Institute of Education, University of London

Midland Examining Group (1988) *Mathematics — General Certificate of Secondary Education Examination Syllabuses 1990*, Cambridge: University of Cambridge, Local Examination Syndicate

Nickson, M. (1992) The Culture of the Mathematics Classroom — an Unknown Quantity? in Grouws, D. (ed) *Handbook of Research on Mathematics Teaching and Learning*, New York: MacMillan

Open University (1986) *Girls into Mathematics*, Milton Keynes: Open University Press

Patrick, H. (1990) *Gender Differences in Public Examination Results*, Paper presented at BERA Conference

Royal Society and the Institute of Mathematics and its Applications (1986) *Girls and Mathematics*, Report by Joint Mathematical Education Committees.

Scott-Hodgetts, R. (1986) Girls and Mathematics: The Negative Implications of Success in Burton L (ed) *Girls into Maths Can Go*, Sussex: Holt Education

Stobart, G., Elwood, J. and Kingdon, M. (1991) *Gender Bias in Examinations: How Equal are the Opportunities?* Paper presented at AEB Research Seminar, University of London Examinations and Assessment Council April 19 1991

Walden, R. and Walkerdine, V. (1982) *Girls and Mathematics: The Early Years*, Bedford Way, Papers 8, Institute of Education, University of London

Walden, R. and Walkerdine, V. (1985) *Girls and Mathematics From Primary to Secondary Schooling*, Bedford Way, Papers 24, Institute of Education, University of London.

CHAPTER FOUR

France

Josette Adda
Catherine Goldstein
Leila Schneps

Introduction

This chapter begins with an overview of the French system of schooling, paying particular attention to the teaching and assessing of mathematics in the context of syllabus development. We then give statistics on the assessment of mathematics, considering three different sources. The first is the baccalauréat, a non-compulsory nation-wide examination taken at the end of the final year of schooling and for which excellent official statistics exist, breaking down the results by many different categories, in particular gender (Ministère de l'Education Nationale, published annually, (b)). The second source is the result of a recent development in French mathematics assessment which aims to assess mathematical skills independently of the competition usually associated with testing, and to serve as an aid for teachers in the evaluation of the strengths and weaknesses of individual students. It consists of a national test administered at the beginning of the school year, in September, to all the students in the country entering a certain grade. The third source is the result of statistics gathered on the entry competitions to the Grandes Ecoles. In the final part we describe the state of the debate over the situation of girls in mathematics and in technological/scientific subjects in general in France, and mention several of the studies and action campaigns which have been or are being conducted.

An overview of the French system of primary and secondary education

French children may go to nursery school as early as two years old. Compulsory schooling begins at age six and must continue until age sixteen, independently of what class the child has reached at that stage. In all, there are twelve grades, or classes in the French terminology; a child enters compulsory school in the calendar year when he/she turns six. The first five years of school are known as CP (Preparatory Class), CE1 and CE2 (Elementary Classes 1 and 2) and CM1 and CM2 (Intermediate Classes 1 and 2). The higher classes are known successively as Sixth, Fifth, Fourth, Third, Second, First and Terminal. It is difficult to associate a particular age with each class because of the high rate of repeating classes which is prevalent in France; 50% of students have repeated at least one year, students who have repeated twice being quite frequent. Many students (particularly boys) leave school at the end of the Third class, in order to work or to attend a vocational school. This affects the statistics on any assessment performed after the Third class, since the boys' scores will benefit from the fact that a selection has already been made at this stage, many of those boys whose scores are lowest having left.

There is no compulsory national leaving exam at any stage of French secondary schooling. The closest thing to it is the baccalauréat; however it is not compulsory, not all students attempt it and of those who do, not all succeed. The statistics for 1990 are as follows: somewhat less than 70% of the adolescents (aged between17 and 20) attempted the baccalauréat and of those who attempted, somewhat less than 70% succeeded; the overall success rate was 44.5% (cf. Ministère de l'Education Nationale, 1991(b)); the government has declared a policy aiming at 80% of students attempting the baccalauréat and a 60% success rate.

At the end of the Second class, students are required to choose among three possibilities for the next year: scientific, literary or technical/vocational, and at the end of the First class they must choose a section leading to a specific baccalauréat: the sections are A (literary), B (economic) for the students who followed a literary First class, C (mathematics/science), D (biology/science) for those who followed a scientific First class, and E (technical) or F and G (vocational) for those who followed a technical first class. The choice of section is made in consultation with teachers, advisers and parents, and it must be noted that the teachers and advisers have a great influence in the making of this choice and that, as will be mentioned later, they play a large role in discouraging many girls from entering the C section.

The C section enjoys extraordinary prestige: it is necessary in order to enter almost any kind of selective school of higher education. Students obtaining their baccalauréat have a choice for further education: they can go to the universities, which are public and non-selective, or, if they are accepted, they can go to a two-year engineering school called IUT, or to one of the prestigious Classes Préparatoires. These are two-to-three year courses preparing students for a strenuous series of competitions for entry into the highly selective Ecoles Normales Supérieures or the Ecole Polytechnique, or the high reputation engineering schools known as the Grandes Ecoles.

The French system of education is balanced between central and local organisation. The syllabus is centrally developed, at the Ministry of Education, and a little booklet containing a detailed description of the syllabus is available to every teacher. However, testing is done within schools, and tests other than the baccalauréat are written by the teachers, the baccalauréat itself being written separately in each scholastic region (academy) by a team of teachers. In France there exists no such thing as a nation-wide exam taken by every student in a given class, unless one counts the assessments given at the beginning of the year to certain classes, instituted in 1990, which will be discussed in the next section.

Assessment in mathematics in France

We discuss below three separate sources of national information: the baccalauréat, a test only taken by those students who have succeeded in continuing their studies until the end of the Terminal year of high school, the national assessments which were introduced only two years ago, and the entry competitions to the Grandes Ecoles. Of these, only the national assessments give any information about differential performances of students in mathematics before the age of 18 and before any kind of selection has been made. The results of all these assessments are public, and can be obtained by writing to the Ministry of Education. The results are broken down into various categories; not only sex but also the social category of the father is considered.

The baccalauréat

A study organised by the Ministry of Education (cf. Ministère de l'Education, (1990(a) of a sample of 19,000 students entering the Sixth class in 1980, showed that 7,000 of them (37%) succeeded in passing the baccalauréat in one of the years 1987, 1988 or 1989. Table I shows how many of those students succeeded in reaching each year of schooling after the Sixth, separated by sex and social category of the father; we see that in every social category, more girls attained every class than boys.

Table II on page 72 presents the results of the 7,000 students who did obtain the baccalauréat, separated by sex. The general baccalauréat (sections A, B, C, D and E) are shown in grey, the technological ones (F and G) in black. This table shows that more girls obtained the general baccalauréat than boys (25% versus 20%), whereas about 6% of each obtained the technological baccalauréat. (Note that the technological baccalauréat contains such sections as 'clothing' and 'hairdressing', the sections F and G are actually vocational sections). When this information is broken down into the different sections, to see what percentage of boys and girls obtained each of the different types of baccalauréat, we obtain Table III (on page 73). The fact that far more boys obtain the mathematical baccalauréat C than girls leaps to the eye. This phenomenon is not a consequence of lower success rates of girls at the exam. On the contrary, their success rate is higher (for the academy of Grenoble in 1989, girls had a 92% rate as opposed to 87% for boys). As shown by S. Gasquet and M. Ruffieux in their book *Lycée: peut mieux faire* (1990), in which they presented a study of six cohorts of students in various lycées in Grenoble, both the high success rate for girls and the low numbers of girls attempting the baccalauréat C can be explained by a process of intensive over-selection at the time of entry into the C section of the lycée leading to preparation of the baccalauréat. As mentioned above, this choice is made at the end of the Second class, but at the end of the First class a student in

70

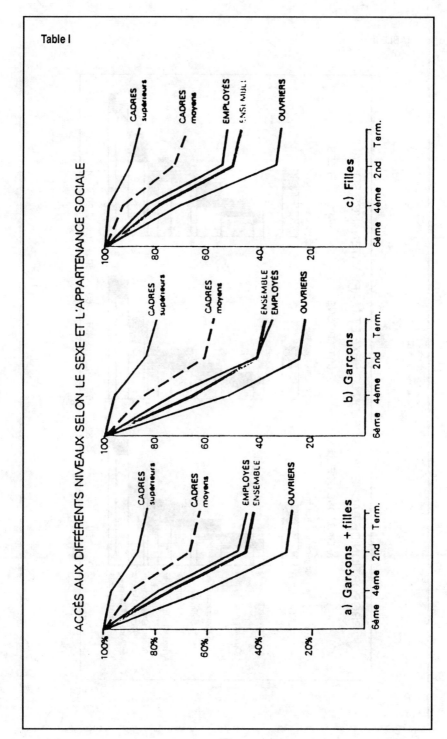

Table I

ACCÈS AUX DIFFÉRENTS NIVEAUX SELON LE SEXE ET L'APPARTENANCE SOCIALE

a) Garçons + filles

b) Garçons

c) Filles

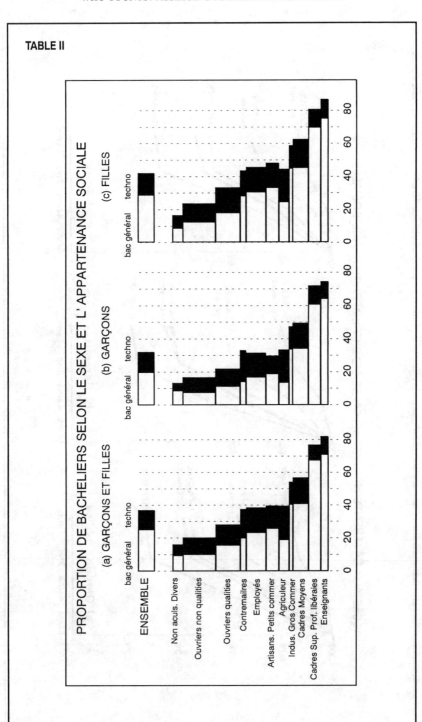

TABLE II

PROPORTION DE BACHELIERS SELON LE SEXE ET L'APPARTENANCE SOCIALE

(a) GARÇONS ET FILLES (b) GARÇONS (c) FILLES

Table III

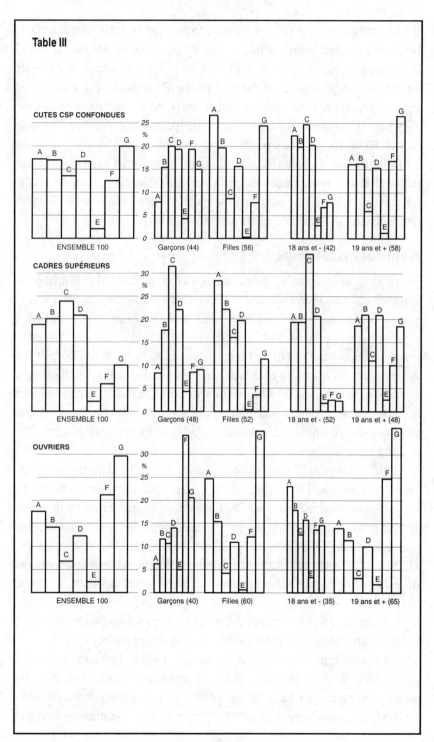

the scientific class can choose whether to pass the baccalauréat C or D, C being considered more difficult. The lycées studied by Gasquet and Ruffieux followed a specific policy of dis-encouragement towards girls who had average results at the end of the First class, and a policy of encouragement to boys with the same results. As a consequence, only the very best girls entered the C section; some lycées even obtained a success rate of 100% for girls as a result of this method.

Table III comes from the official statistics from the Ministry of Education for the percentages of girls and boys in each section of the baccalauréat. It would seem that the phenomenon observed by Gasquet and Ruffieux in Grenoble exists at a national level.

National assessments

In 1990, a new form of assessment was created by the Ministry of Education. Tests in French and mathematics were administered to every student entering the school year CE2 and the Sixth class, and to a representative group of students entering the Third year. These tests were given in September, 1990 and were intended to be analysed both at the government level and by each teacher. On an individual level, their goal was not to test the students but simply to evaluate their level, in order to help both teacher and student have a better idea of their strengths and weaknesses. A similar test was administered to students entering the Second class in September 1992.

Table IV on page 75 shows test scores for the CE2 and Sixth class tests, both in French and in mathematics, broken down by sex and also by subject published in *Education et Formation*, Ministère de l'Education 1990(a). We do not discuss the results in French other than to remark the unquestionable superiority of girls on these tests. The results of the mathematics tests show nearly negligible differences between the scores of girls and boys, girls doing better in some sections and boys in others. In the Sixth class test, it is notable that the girls have a very slightly higher average score than the boys in the mathematical subsection 'geometry', traditionally considered to be a domain of male superiority.

A different type of table presents results of the test given in the Third class (Table V, page 76), with the scores in mathematics broken down by socio-professional category of the father. In the categories considered to be most favourable for education of children, and among students who had

Table IV

TABLEAU: MOYENNE DES ECARTS DES SCORES ENTRE FILLES ET GARCONS TOUS AGES CONFONDUS AU CE2

Disciplines	Filles	Garcons	Ecarts F?G (en %)
Francais/88	60,5	55,5	+ 9,0
— comprehension/25	15,9	14,6	+ 9,1
— connaissance du code/49	34,4	31,4	+ 9,5
— production de texte/14	10,1	9,5	+7,1
Mathematiques/71	57,1	57,2	-0,3
— geometrie/10	6,3	6,4	-1,4
— mesures/14	7,9	7,8	+0,5
— travaux numeriques/47	31,9	32.0	-0,3

TABLEAU: MOYENNE DES ECARTS DES SCORES ENTRE FILLES ET GARCONS TOUS AGES CONFONDUS EN 6eme

Francais/107	59,5	53,5	+11,4
comprehension/15	10,7	10,3	+ 3,5
unites constitutives du mot/7	3.9	3,2	+20,1
lexique/17	9,0	8,5	+ 5,6
morphosyntaxe/18	9,1	7,6	+19,2
structure phrase texte/22	9,7	8,3	+16,7
production-expression/28	17,3	15,5	+11,4
Mathematiques/97	71,0	70,5	+ 0,7
numeration et nbres deci/26	18,8	18,9	- 0,8
techniques opératoires/9	6,8	6,4	+ 5,8
sens des operations/13	9,1	9,1	- 0,4
figures geometriques/10	8,1	8,1	+ 0,1
reception-trait-production/39	28,2	27,9	+ 1,1

not repeated any classes, the girls did quite a bit better than the boys but in the other social classes and, particularly among students who had to repeat classes, the girls were well behind. This is one of the strongest indications as to the influence of socio-professional category on the situation of girls and mathematics; parents whose work does not require a high level of education are less likely to have girls doing mathematics and this is certainly no coincidence. Finally, in Table VI on page 76 we give the mean gaps and distributions of the results of these tests, which give an immediate visual impression of the nature of the differentiated results.

Table V: SCORE MOYEN OBTENU AUX EPREUVES DE MATHEMATIQUES EN TROISIEME SELON L'AGE LE SEXE ET LA CATEGORIE SOCIALE DU PERE

(sur 200) Categorie sociale du pere	Garcons a l'heure	Filles a l'heure	Garcons en retard	Filles en retard
Agriculteurs	94.1	113.3	96.0	59.9
Independants	108.8	115.7	86.0	83.0
Cadres superieurs	136.0	131.0	105.5	90.6
Cadres moyens	126.4	117.9	96.7	83.4
Employes	126.3	112.4	94.6	85.1
Ouvriers	103.1	100.4	85.9	74.9
Ensemble	121.9	116.2	92.4	81.1

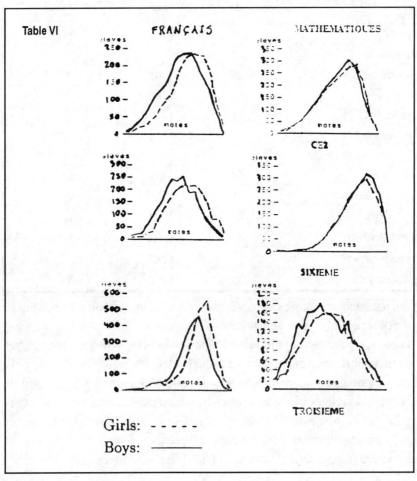

Table VI

FRANÇAIS — MATHEMATIQUES — CE2 — SIXIEME — TROISIEME

Girls: - - - - -

Boys: ———

The competitions for the Grandes Ecoles

Around 30% of the students in the first two years of the scientific sections of the universities and 18% in the prestigious and competitive CPGE ('classes préparatoires aux Grandes Ecoles') are women. The French system creates an abyss of difference between these two types of formation, as only the CPGE prepare the students for the entry competitions to the prestigious scientific and engineering schools (Grandes Ecoles). Until recently, there were virtually no points of similarity between the two systems: location (the CPGE are usually in secondary schools while the university campuses are sprawling and overcrowded), class size (similar to secondary school for the CPGE, whereas university lectures are often to groups of over 200 students), type of work (more hours in the CPGE, with extra time for individual oral sessions and more difficult and competitive work), job prospects (guaranteed in principle to any student who succeeds in entering, and graduating from an engineering school) and salaries. The universities were, in practice, reserved for the less talented (or less rapid or less hard-working) students, or the exotic ones who could or would not stand the strain of the CPGE In particular, the students holding a D-baccalauréat in natural sciences were more numerous in the universities, while most students in the CPGE hold the C-baccalauréat.

In the last few years, this rigid system has become very slightly more supple. For example, alternative curricula such as engineering classes preparing entry to the Grandes Ecoles have been held in the universities. This corresponds to a change in the job market. The increasing necessity for qualified engineers implies that mathematics and computer science education is necessary for a greater number of students and this has not been sufficiently taken into account by engineering schools which continue to be excessively selective. However, in the main, the choice of CPGE or university continues to be a deep and nearly unbridgeable division, leading to different careers.

It should be noted that, though there are already few enough girls in the first year of the CPGE, many choose not to continue into the second year, although there is no actual exam to be passed, or they choose the easier sections which do not prepare the entrance competitions to the most prestigious schools such as the Ecole Polytechnique or the Ecole Normale Supérieure in Lyon or the one in Paris, which is the one leading most directly to a career in scientific research (the situation for girls and boys in the CPGE is not identical; boys are lodged in the school itself whereas many schools do not have rooming facilities for girls who must seek lodging elsewhere, although this situation has been improving recently). Until 1986, the situation was entirely different as each Ecole Normale Supérieure consisted of two separate schools for the different sexes, with separate entrance competitions. The students at these schools, once they had entered, followed a common curriculum and took the same courses, therefore the system actually worked like a quota system. It is often cited as being one of the main reasons for the relatively large number of women research mathematicians in France. But in 1986, the entrance exams in all subjects became mixed. The consequences in mathematics are particularly severe. Out of 40 students per year accepted to the Ecole Normale Supérieure in Paris in mathematics since 1986, between 1 and 4 are women, whereas previously a total of 50-60 students were accepted into the separate schools, of which about 20 were women. These results are too recent to have received a satisfactory explanation: they could be a consequence of the fact that although there is a mean level of 18% of women in the CPGE classes, that level is actually far smaller in the few most prestigious ones which prepare the Ecole Normale Supérieure. The number of women candidates has also decreased — entrance competitions for all engineering schools take place in roughly the same period, putting tremendous stress on the students, and many women may consider it a waste of time and effort to try an exam where so few women succeed.

An entirely different but promising line of research indicates that the competitive, stressful system of entrance competitions is less acceptable to and for women. For example, extreme rapidity is encouraged despite the observation that women tend to work on each question longer, spending more time trying to solve it, before skipping to the next one. Therefore they often do not pick up the scattering of points obtained by writing a few remarks on each different question.

Table VII on page 80 gives the results for the mixed entrance competitions for the Ecole Normale Superieure in Paris, in all subjects. Group A is mathematics, B physics, C biology, S social sciences and L literature and classics. As comparison, the results for the Ecole Normale Superieure in Lyon were 3 women accepted in mathematics and 31 men, 12 women and 21 men in physics, out of a total of 116 women candidates and 604 men candidates.

From Table VIII on page 81 giving the percentages of men and women among university students, it can be noticed that the percentage of women in the second year of university is higher than in the first. Entry into the second year is decided by an examination: it would seem that this does not prevent women from succeeding. Perhaps strict scientific results are not as important as the choices involved. Or perhaps more men do not succeed in the university examinations at the end of the first year because they are only the worst students, those who could not enter the CPGE, whereas many women choose the university over the CPGE for other reasons than their poor performance. There have been some local studies investigating these factors (Cousquer, 1991).

On the other hand, the association of mathematics with physics which predominates in France, especially in the CPGE, seems particularly unfortunate for girls, whose loathing of physics exceeds even their dislike for mathematics. The university permits mathematics to be studied with biology or with the social sciences; these options contain a higher percentage of women. A rather recent phenomenon is the increasing proportion of successful women in economic and commercial schools, including the most prestigious ones such as the HEC.

Table VIII (page 81) shows the distribution of men and women in the universities, by age and subject. As pointed out in the preceding discussion, the difference between the number of men and women in the university choosing to study the sciences is minimal compared with the CPGE.

The debate on girls and mathematics in France

Statistics concerning the presence of girls in the various scientific curricula have been an object of study in France for several years. The debate is becoming quite general, partly because of the urgent need in France for more qualified science teachers and engineers; every mathematics teacher in France has probably become caught up in it. It has become socially unacceptable to declare that girls are less capable in mathematics than boys. However, deep-rooted prejudices still remain. A teacher in a medium-sized provincial town, recently interviewed by a member of *Femmes et Mathématiques*, said that in his experience girls and boys performed equally well until about the end of the Second class, and then during the year of the First class, the girls fell far behind. He noted that

Table VII				
	Inscris	Admissibles	Admis (l. pr.)	Entrés
Groupe A				
Garçons	698	137	40	42
Filles	117	7	1	2
Groups B				
Garçons	432	53	22	21
Filles	76	5	1	3
Groupe C				
Garçons	186	39	12	13
Filles	243	24	10	10
Groupe S				
Garçons	122	24	15	15
Filles	123	19	6	6
Groupe L				
Garçons	318	73	32	32
Filles	649	84	44	44

only in the First class are the students asked to solve problems applying several logical steps, rather than only one. He did not say that he considered girls to be incapable of performing several logical steps, but it seemed to be implied. However, the question is frequently and openly discussed and the statistics presented in the preceding section are beginning to be widely known. The teachers' group APMEP (Association des Professeurs de Mathématiques de l'Enseignement Public) is particularly interested in the problem and distributes information for teachers and students. The president of this association changes every one or two years and is frequently a woman; it is worth noting also that the proportion of women among mathematics teachers is growing (49.9% of mathematics teachers in secondary schools were women in 1989-90). We present below a series of studies and action campaigns which have been initiated in recent years.

Table VIII: EFFECTS UNIVERSITAIRES PAR SEXE, DISCIPLINE ET AGE EN 1989-1990 (France metropolitaine)

Hommes	18 ans et moins	19 et 20 ans	21 et 22 ans	23 et 24 ans	25 et 26 ans	27 et 28 ans	29 et 30 ans	31 ans et plus	%	Ensemble Effectifs (%)
Droit	7.5	26.0	22.6	15.2	8.3	4.8	3.6	12.0	100.0	65 988
Sciences economiques, AES	7.4	28.9	27.2	15.7	6.8	3.7	2.6	7.7	100.0	57 515
Lettres, sciences humaines	4.9	19.0	19.0	13.9	9.4	6.8	5.4	21.5	100.0	106 364
Sciences, MASS	10.6	24.4	23.8	15.0	8.7	5.3	3.6	8.7	100.0	140 380
Médecine	4.7	11.7	9.3	9.5	11.4	11.3	12.5	29.5	100.0	61 210
Pharmacie	6.8	22.6	17.8	15.2	13.1	7.9	5.2	11.4	100.0	10 921
Odontologie	0.2	5.7	15.7	20.8	19.0	11.1	6.6	20.9	100.0	5 645
Pluridisciplinaire, STAPS	11.1	30.9	22.5	12.4	6.7	4.0	2.7	9.6	100.0	19 132
IUT	14.3	55.8	22.8	4.0	1.3	0.6	0.4	0.8	100.0	44 459
Ensemble, toutes disciplines	**8.1**	**25.2**	**21.0**	**13.2**	**8.4**	**5.8**	**4.7**	**13.7**	**100.0**	**511 614**

Femmes	18 ans et moins	19 et 20 ans	21 et 22 ans	23 et 24 ans	25 et 26 ans	27 et 28 ans	29 et 30 ans	31 ans et plus	%	Ensemble Effectifs
Droit	11.9	32.1	24.1	13.7	6.1	3.1	2.0	7.0	100.0	83 541
Sciences economiques, AES	12.2	35.5	29.2	12.7	4.1	1.9	1.1	3.3	100.0	52 829
Lettres, sciences humaines	9.6	27.5	21.9	13.4	7.3	4.2	3.0	13.1	100.0	257 458
Sciences, MASS	13.5	27.7	24.0	14.5	7.3	4.0	2.4	6.6	100.0	73 739
Médecine	9.6	18.1	12.9	11.6	12.2	10.9	8.1	16.6	100.0	53 869
Pharmacie	13.5	26.4	18.3	17.4	10.8	4.8	2.8	5.9	100.0	19 752
Odontologie	0.3	10.4	20.5	25.2	17.6	8.7	4.7	12.5	100.0	3 818
Pluridisciplinaire, STAPS	16.0	35.8	19.6	9.4	4.9	3.0	2.4	8.7	100.0	22 834
IUT	19.2	55.7	18.0	3.4	1.3	0.7	0.5	1.1	100.0	25 435
Ensemble, toutes disciplines	**11.4**	**29.4**	**21.9**	**13.0**	**7.1**	**4.3**	**2.9**	**10.0**	**100.0**	**593 275**

Opération 50 Lycées

In order better to understand the attitudes, choices and opinions of high school students, and thus the circumstances which lead them so massively to avoid scientific curricula, the French association 'Mathématiques à Venir' (Mathematics of the Future), a grouping of five professional associations (including *Femmes et Mathématiques*) of mathematicians and mathematics teachers at every level, in 1989 undertook a large-scale survey on the image of mathematics and mathematicians among high school students, called *Opération 50 Lycées*. Fifty high schools with 2500 students from all over France, randomly selected, were involved in the study. The questions touched directly on mathematical activities in the classroom. For instance, did the students consider it normal to spend more than an hour solving a problem, or, how difficult did they consider the mathematics courses at various levels. Questions were also asked about mathematics as a free-time activity, on careers and on personal estimates of mathematical talents, school results, and so forth. There was no attempt to compare the answers of the students expressing their own opinions with their objective performance as reflected by grades in school or on special tests.

The results do reveal a visible separation between girls and boys. The girls are far more critical of the selective role played by mathematics in secondary and higher education. Among students saying that they have good results in mathematics, 62% of the girls versus 45% of the boys think that mathematics is excessively important as a criteria for selection.

On the other hand, girls are more numerous than boys in believing that a 'gift' for mathematics exists — and that they do not have it, regardless of their performance in class! Here are some significant items:

Do you think that a 'gift' for mathematics exists, given once and for all, or do you think that it is possible to develop such a gift?

70% of boys believe it can be developed
59% of girls believe it can be developed

What do you think of your own results in mathematics?

60% of boys believe their results are good or very good
51% of girls believe their results are good or very good

Regardless of your results, do you think that you are gifted in mathematics?

71% of boys answered Yes

50% of girls answered Yes

Among those who believe that the gift for mathematics is given once and for all, 28% of the boys and 62% of the girls do not think they have it.

Another important point raised by the study is the following: girls who say that their results in mathematics are good do not necessarily think of themselves as talented, still less as future scientists. Far more than for boys, interest and results in mathematics seem to be dissociated from career projects. For instance, although 86% and 89% of the boys studied in the *Opération 50 Lycées* think that mathematics is a necessary part of one's studies, only 73% of the girls, as opposed to 87% of boys, say that they would actually take a mathematics course if it was not obligatory.

The Nantes study

In the Nantes study directed by C. Baudelot, students from several local terminal classes were interviewed and followed over a period of time. This study underscores the particularly strong differences between girls and boys whose performance in mathematics is average (rather than excellent or poor). In this medium range, boys are better and more deeply engaged in mathematics than girls.

Students in their last year of high school, aiming to pass the *baccalauréat* at the end of the year, find themselves in one of many different sections labelled A through F, according to the type of baccalauréat they will pass. As mentioned earlier, the C-section is the most difficult and prestigious, leading to the Baccalauréat C in mathematics. The results of the study show that there are far fewer differences between girls and boys chosen only from the C-section than between girls and boys randomly chosen from all sections. However, nearly all the girls (but *not* the boys) from the C- section claim that since they have been in school they have never had any problems in mathematics. This reflects the phenomenon of excessive selection: only the very best among the girls are encouraged to enter the C-section, whereas any boy showing talent or interest is encouraged, almost compelled to enter.

83

Allez les Filles!

Christian Baudelot, the director of the Nantes study, together with another sociologist Roger Establet, gathered together numerous statistics from different studies, and from the evaluations mentioned in the preceding section, and wrote a book called *Allez les Filles!* ((Baudelot and Establet, 1991)). This book is meant to be read by everyone, rather than being specifically directed towards didacticians and teachers, as is unfortunately the case with many of the other studies, whose contents were never made fully public. It has had a great success in France, encouraged by local actions such as visits by Baudelot to various provincial towns for public discussion. The main point of the book, which does not concentrate on mathematics but which does contain an entire chapter devoted to it, is to show that statistics frankly contradict the deep-rooted conviction of many people that girls are less capable in mathematics than boys. The conclusions he draws are that there is no difference in mathematical capacity and that the profound differences in choices of orientation which appear around the age of fifteen are mainly due to social pressures of various kinds.

Secretariat of Women's Rights

The Secrétariat d'Etat aux Droits des Femmes, the government section for women's rights in France, has recently launched certain programmes in order to encourage girls to continue scientific studies. In 1986, they created a special scholarship called 'Bourse de la Vocation', given to fifty girls each year, to encourage them to choose scientific or technical curricula. In 1991, this policy was decentralised and now each region has an office working on the problem and the national scholarship is replaced by a departmental prize, the 'Prix de la Vocation' awarded to girls in the Terminal class of high school. The prize of 5000 French francs is more a symbolic than a financial incentive.

Some of the regional offices have worked hard to develop a campaign called 'C'est Technique, C'est Pour Elles' (It's technical, it's for girls). This campaign consists in visits to high schools, distribution of T-shirts, posting of large and attractive posters, and distribution of a video interviewing girls who have technical jobs and are successful in them. Students interested by the campaign are encouraged to go to the regional offices of orientation counselling, where trained counsellors have information about all the possible curricula for higher study, as well as about jobs in technology. Indeed the State Secretariat for Women's Rights is seeking to negotiate contacts with companies to ensure the hiring of girls in scientific and technical areas.

Other Programmes

Two European programmes (Tenet, cf. (Junter-Loiseau, 1991)) have been set up in France, in Rennes and in Alsace-Lorraine (this last in conjunction with a group in Brussels). In each case, informational meetings for career counsellors and teachers have been arranged. The second of the two programmes aims particularly at problems of orientation in work and study, and decisions taken in class councils. The first is oriented more towards the high-school students themselves, through questions concerning their role models and their image of a scientific career. This study has revealed that, for girls, improved integration into their mathematics class, and even improved performance, does not necessarily correspond to an increased desire to embark on a scientific career.

We must emphasise that various French mathematical societies have been seeking for some years to draw attention to the need to recruit mathematicians at all levels as a response to the economic challenge facing the country. Teachers of mathematics in particular will be in enormous demand during the coming decade. Far more will be needed than the number of students now preparing to be mathematics teachers. For this reason among others, vigorous campaigns encouraging girls to take up mathematical and scientific training are meeting with a favourable response.

The association *Femmes et Mathématiques*, formed in 1987, has been particularly involved in informing the public about these questions and on approaching students to improve the image of women mathematicians and of mathematics as a career. Many different types of action have been undertaken, for example local meetings between students and women scientists in all areas have been arranged, and interviews with women mathematicians and scientists have been published in widely read magazines. The idea that mathematics is a possible, suitable, and fascinating field for women as well as men will, it is hoped, soon be seen by parents, teachers and counsellors, as completely acceptable rather than as a contradiction to familiar tradition.

References

Baudelot, C. and Establet, R. (1991) *Allez les Filles!*, Ed.Le Seuil.

Cousquer, E. (1991) *L'orientation scolaire et professionnelle filles dans l'Académic de Lille*, UFR de Mathématiques de l'Université de Lille 1, 59655 Villeneuve d'Ascq Cedex.

Gasquet, S. and Ruffieux, M. (1990) *Lycée: peut mieux faire*, Syros Alternatives.

Junter-Loiseau, A. (1991) *Se former à l'egalité des chances entre filles et garçons*, report on the Tenet program at the Rennes Academy, CRDP, Paris.

Ministère de l'Education (undated a), *Education et Formation* Nationale, Nos. 23 June, 1990 and 27 August, 1991.

Ministère de l'Education Nationale (b). *Repères et références statistiques sur les enseignements et la formation* DEP.

Vouillot, F. (ed.) (1991) *L'orientation scolaire et professionnelle*, Special Issue on 'Pourquoi si peu de filles en sciences?', published by the INETOP, rue Gay-Lussac, October.

Complementary Bibliography

The following bibliography includes only papers and books having appeared in France since 1986. They often offer relevant references themselves, which we do not repeat. Other important sources not contained in this bibliography are those given in the preceding list of references and also the publications of various specialised associations such as *Femmes et Mathématiques*, the Association des femmes diplômées, the Association pour une éducation non-sexiste, the Association des Femmes Ingénieurs, etc.

Books

L'exercice du savoir et la différence des sexes, (1991) coll. Paris: L'Harmattan.

Campbell, A. (éd.) (1990) *Masculin, Féminin, Mieux vivre avec l'autre*, Paris: Larousse.

Duru-Belllat, M. (1990) *L'école des filles, Quelle formation pour quels rôles sociaux?*, Paris: L'Harmattan.

Mosconi, N. (1989) *La Mixité dans l'enseignement secondaire: un faux- semblant*, Paris: PUF

Reports and studies

Mathématiques A Venir, *Bulletin de la Société Mathématique de France*, Supplément, tome 115, Gauthier-Villars, Paris, 1987.

Mathématiques A Venir, *Les maths et vous*, rapport de l'enquête réalisée par G. Barbançon, R. Duval, C. Dupuis et F. Pluvinage, IREM de Strasbourg, 1988.

Recherches sur les femmes et recherches féministes, Action Thématique Programmée du CNRS, Présentation des travaux 1986-1989, 1990.

Femmes et Sciences, Special Issue of *Autrement*, September 1992.

Les objectifs de la formation scientifique, Acts of the Colloquium of April 28-29, 1990, Palaiseau.

Femmes et mathématiques, Information Brochure, November 1991.

Association française des femmes diplômées des Universités, 'La formation du personnel de l'enseignement secondaire à l'égalité des chances entre filles et garçons', *Diplômées*, trimestrial revue, no. 158, September 1991.

Secrétariat d'Etat aux Droit des Femmes, 'Sciences et Techniques écrivent l'avenir. Moi aussi', publicity campaign consisting of information and brochures, April 1991.

Vouillot, F. (éd.) (1991) 'Sciences et techniques, pourquoi si peu de filles', *L'Orientation Scolaire et Professionnelle,* September, vol. 20-3.

Papers

J. Adda, 'Is gender a relevant variable for mathematics education? (The Case of the French Situation). Paper given at the ICMI Study Conference, Höör, Sweden, October, 1993.

V. Aebischer, 'Disciplines scientifiques et projets professionels', *Bulletin de l'Association des Professeurs de Mathématiques*, no. 366, December 1988.

C. Baudelot, 'Aimez-vous les maths?', *Journées internationales d'analyse de données textuelles,* Barcelona, 1990.

N. Bécarud, 'La femme dans le monde de la science et de la technique', Association française des femmes diplômées des Universités, *Diplômées, Trimestrial Revue*, no. 143, December 1987.

C. Bedarida and C. Helfter, 'Filles: la fausse réussite scolaire', *Le Monde de l'Education,* no 173, July-August 1990, 18-36.

D. Bonora and M. Huteau, 'L'efficience comparée des garçons et des filles en mathématiques', in 'Sciences et techniques, pourquoi si peu de filles', F. Vouillot, éd., *L'Orientation Scolaire et Professionnelle*, September 1991, vol. 20-3, 269-290.

M. T. Bournival, 'La passion des équations', *La Gazette des Femmes*, vol. 11, no. 4, November-December 1989.

S. Chaperon, 'Le deuxième sexe est tertiaire et le premier secondaire', *Le Mouvement Social*, no. 140, July-September 1987.

M. F. Coste-Roy, 'La place des femmes dans les mathématiques', *Bulletin de la Société Mathématique de France,* Supplement, tome 115, Gauthier-Villars, Paris, 1987, 320-342.

A. M. Daune-Richard, 'Les facteurs d'émergence de trajectoires de sexe atypiques', *Colloque sur l'Economie du Travail Féminin* Madrid, December 1988, Laboratoire d'Economie et de Sociologie du Travail, Aix-en-Provence.

A.M. Daune-Richard et C. Marry, 'Autres histoires de transfuges?', *Formation-Emplois*, no. 29, January-March 1990, 35-50.

M. Duthoit, 'Modes de fréquentation du collège: bilan quantitif des scolarités d'un echantillon de 20000 élèves', *Education et Formations*, no. 23, April-June 1990, 21-32.

C. Goldstein, 'Des filles et des sciences', *Journal de l'Opération 50 Lycées*, no. 3, 1989.

I. Marchi-Barbaux, 'La Lorraine scientifique et technique... avec les femmes', *Economie Lorraine*, no. 77, March 1989.

C. Marry, 'Femmes Ingénieurs: une (ir)résistible ascension?', *Information sur les Sciences Sociales*, SAGE Publications, vol. 28-2, June 1989.

J. Peiffer, 'L'engouement des femmes pour les sciences au XVIIème siècle', *Femmes et pouvoirs sous l'ancien régime*, D. Haase- Dubosc et E. Viennot, éd., Rivages/Histoire, Paris, 1991.

J. Peiffer, 'La place réservée aux femmes en sciences exactes et appliquées: place aveugle ou non-lieu', *Perspectives Universitaires*, vol. III, 1-2, pp. 113-136, 1986.

A. Servant, 'Apprentissages fondamentaux en fin de 5ème. Nature et évaluation des acquis, liens avec le vécu et le cursus scolaire', *Education et Formations* no. 24, July-September 1990, 31-43.

M.A. Vigan, 'Femmes et Mathématiques', *Cahiers du Féminisme* no. 56, spring 1991, 38-39.

CHAPTER FIVE

The Federal Republic of Germany

Christine Keitel
Gabriele Kaiser-Meßmer

The Educational System in Germany

The federal constitution of Germany and the 'cultural autonomy' of the individual states mean that regulations for school education and the access to schools as well as decisions on curricula (syllabi and textbooks), resources and payment of teachers are made independently by each of the states. Differing historical roots of education in the different states have led to a variety of education regulations and syllabi or programmes which by agreement at the level of the ministries of education, are brought into mutual acceptability and equivalence.

The predominant characteristic of the German educational system is that it is tripartite.[1] All children attend 4 years of primary school[2] which are followed by a choice out of three types of secondary schools. These are Volksschule or Hauptschule (HS) which only leads to vocational education parallel to an apprenticeship in industry or craftmanship, Realschule (RS, middle school of secondary level or lower technical school) which aims at banking, commercial and technical vocations or prepares for Technische Fachschulen (Technical Highschools) and Gymnasia (G, Upper Secondary or Grammar Schools) with a strict scientific or academic orientation.[3]

Before the educational reform in the 60s, the different names for the school subject mathematics, namely arithmetic for primary and Hauptschule, and mathematics for higher secondary, clearly underlined the differences in quality and quantity of knowledge offered in secondary schooling. In mathematics education much more rigidly than in all other school subjects, not only the amount but also the quality of the knowledge provided, depended on the type of school attended. There were two underlying assumptions which supported the highly selective function of mathematics to discriminate between future opportunities and their related social status. The pupil in Hauptschule was assumed to be unable to acquire more than very restricted knowledge (and no mathematics at all!); also this pupil was assumed not to need any more mathematics for future vocational or private life. Until the late 1960s, schooling was compulsory for 8 years in Hauptschule, followed by 3 years vocational schooling as part of a formal apprenticeship for the successful school leaver. For Realschule pupils, 10 years was followed by 2 or 3 years further education in special commercial or technical highschools, while the university-bound secondary Gymnasium pupil continued to the 13th grade. The characteristic of the German school system which is to separate, select and sort pupils, results in a high proportion of children being sent to special needs schools.[4]

This chapter examines the impact of the assessment mode in mathematics on achievement, and in particular its effects on girls' self-concept, attitudes, behaviour and beliefs, and the outcomes when choosing careers.

The mathematics teachers

The strength of the teaching force within a country depends heavily on three factors. First is the degree of professionalisation provided by the teacher training system. Second are the social conditions offered to the profession, the degree of professional autonomy, freedom and self-determination. Third, is social status represented partly by social recognition, the financial resources provided for their work, and their salary. The mathematics teacher in the states of the Federal Republic of Germany enjoys a high social status, which is partly given by the social aₗ preciation of the subject of mathematics, partly by her/his status as a public servant. After passing the 5-6 years of preservice training at the university (the first phase of teacher training) and the 2 years at the practical seminary (the second phase of teacher training), in comparison to most other countries a long and intensive preparation, including two state examinations, and after successfully applying for a post in a school of a type s/he has chosen but decided by the state, the teacher of mathematics (for all school types) enters a profession with considerable autonomy and freedom.

Although s/he has to pay attention to a *state-determined syllabus* (which differs for the different school types of the tripartite system and for every state), these syllabi are a mixture of prescription (of certain topics) and recommendation (of methodological approaches, hours for themes, etc.) and function mainly as a *guideline for teaching*. Commercially produced textbooks have to be closely related to the syllabi and to concretise and 'explain' them. The colleagues at the school together choose those most appropriate for their pupils from a selection of textbooks (which in many states in Germany are provided by the school for pupils on loan), or use teaching materials produced by the teacher and/or their colleagues. The teacher decides on teaching style, how to mark homework and oral or written classwork as well as on the annual promotion of the pupils. With the exception of a very few states such as Bavaria and Baden-Württemberg which have central state examinations at the end of schooling and more state control on the teaching and marking of their teachers, the teacher is trusted to assess pupils' performance and achievement and to evaluate their teaching by *school- and teacher-based assessment modes* only. In secondary schooling teachers' obligations are focused on the teaching of the subject matter rather than being connected with pedagogical or formative expectations. The teaching hours are fixed at between about 24 (for higher secondary schools of the *Gymnasium* type) up to about 28 (for lower secondary schools such as *Hauptschule* and primary schools). A teacher in service looks forward to the prospect of a *well-paid tenured position as a state employee*; their salary is seen as the second best in the world and is not comparable to that of most colleagues even in Western countries. A broad offering of *inservice training* and further education is provided by the state, too, *for volunteers*.

Educational reforms of the 60s

The rebuilding of the German educational system immediately after world war II consisted of a reconstruction of what had existed in the 1920s including the separation between mathematics and arithmetic for the different school types. A new orientation of educational policy on mathematics and science education in schools started in 1968 (Damerow 1977, Howson et al.1981, Keitel 1980) with the 'Recommendations and Guidelines for the Modernisation of Mathematics Instruction in Primary and Secondary schools in the FRG' of the Kultusministerkonferenz (KMK) (standing conference of the ministers of cultural affairs of the FRG). This change to an active educational policy of reform of mathematics education, which had started in the USA and Great Britain in the 1950s and was reinforced by OECD for other European countries, was based on the following goals:

— improving and *raising the scientific standard of school mathematics* according to the standard set up by the development of the academic discipline of mathematics;

— raising the general standard of education for the majority of the population in designing a *basic general education in science and mathematics;*

— *activating more of the educational resources* of the whole nation by encouraging lower social class pupils, and particularly girls, to follow studies in higher education;

— increasing the *interchangeability* of the elements of the educational system, that is principal access to higher education and to universities from each track of the system.

The crucial and decisive novelty of this political decision was the fact that school mathematics in all school types was regarded as a unity. This became a basis for attempts at general integration but an integration related to the curricular level; the integration of the three educational tracks should not be done via a restructuring of the tripartite system but via the development of a *comprehensive mathematical curriculum*, common and *unified but differentiated,* for all school types — mathematics for all! (Keitel 1987, 1989, 1990). In addition, a campaign to encourage pupils into higher secondary education caused an expansion of the Gymnasium. Compulsory schooling was extended to grade 9 or 10 depending upon the state, and a few experimental comprehensive schools (Gesamt-schule, GS) which offered lower and higher secondary schooling in different tracks within one school type were established parallel to the tripartite system in some of the states.

The expansion of the 13 years-Gymnasia to a broader public and the establishment of comprehensive schools had a big influence on the distribution of the school population. The Hauptschule slowly became a 'remainders' school with enormous disciplinary problems and very low achievement standards, and for ideological reasons the comprehensive school and the Gymnasium were forced to compete in a manner which discriminated against the comprehensive school.

The following data show the changes in school population per type from 1966 and 1988 giving the mean figure across the country and the range of differences between states

School types	1966	1988	Range of differences in 1988
Hauptschule (HS)	62%	34%	16%-45%
Realschule (RS)	18%	27%	21%-35%
Gymnasium (G)	20%	30%	27%-35%
Sonderschule (S)	4%	4%	
Gesamtschule (GS)		5%	1%-28%*
* Berlin 28%; Hamburg 18%; Hesse 15%; Bremen 9%; Northrhine-Westphalia 6%; other <5% (Rösner 1989)			

In 1991, the proportion of girls to boys was 45% to 55% in the Hauptschule (HS), 51.5% to 48.5% in Realschule (RS), and 53% to 47% in the Gymnasium (G) with a surplus of boys in the whole school population. The ratio between girls and boys was 36% to 64% among the school leavers without general secondary certificate of Hauptschule, and 39% to 61% without the certificate of the Realschule. The yearly retention rate in 1984/85 was about 2% in primary and HS, 5% in RS, and 4% in

Gymnasium. Retention rates have diminished in the last 10 years because of legal actions taken by parents which have resulted in the application of tight regulations on retention.

Principles of assessment in the German school system

Assessment modes in German schools can vary very much. Teaching and assessing are seen as a unit, assessment almost universally teacher-based. Each mathematics teacher is allowed to design and use her own assessment modes and criteria within very few constraints stipulated in the school laws of each state. The tripartite system however makes assessment a crucial determinant for the development of the pupil and her future career. Are teachers aware of this far reaching influence? In the following we refer to the school law of Hesse, recently enacted (Hessisches Schulgesetz 1993) which represents the typical thinking about assessment issues in the current German school administration and the debate among teachers.

Teacher-based assessment:

By law, all teachers are obliged to evaluate their teaching and assess the achievement of their pupils by their own assessment methods. The assessment has to consider achievement in the subject as well as the working attitude and social behaviour of the individual pupil. The assessment is based on the continuous observation of the pupil's participation in teacher-guided instruction, on homework and the results of written 'classwork' i.e. tests. The results of the assessment procedure have to be given to the pupils and parents every half year in a written report. Each individual report mainly consists of grades for each subject (range 1 = excellent, 2 = good, 3 = satisfactory, 4 = sufficient, 5 = deficient, 6 = poor or insufficient, with 5 or 6 as fail), and grades about the general development and the behaviour of the pupil during the term which might be replaced by written comments. The pupils have to be informed by the teachers of their grades in advance, might discuss them, and in some cases can renegotiate them. The decision as to whether a pupil can proceed to the next class or whether she or he has to repeat is based on the reported grades at the end of the school year. It is stated in the school law how many failing grades (5 or 6) dictate retention as well as how many good grades in which subjects might compensate for other bad grades. Crucial for retention is the discrimination between the core subjects (mathematics, German language and literature, first and second foreign language, physics or history) and the 'less important' subjects like art, music, sport. It is usually only possible to compensate for one failing grade in a core subject with good grades in at least two less important subjects.

The school law, administrative rules or official guidelines prescribe the minimum number of formal written classworks in the core subjects in each school year. In the less important subjects, the school conference (a democratic institution within each school made up of 1/3 teachers, 1/3 pupils, 1/3 parents and the head) decides whether written, more formal tests have to be carried out). For example, in mathematics at level 5-6, six to eight written classworks lasting at least one hour of lesson time are prescribed, at level 7-8, five to seven, at level 9-10, five to six written classworks lasting at least two hours of lesson time have to be done.[5]

In addition many teachers can and do use shorter informal achievement 'tests'. Guidelines also prescribe the ratio of oral to written performance; oral assessment grades count 50%-75% in lower classes, but this goes down to 50%-30% in higher classes; written assessment counts for 50% in the final grading of the core subjects. In the less important subjects (including biology, history, geography etc. in lower secondary), the written assessment counts for one-third of the final grading. In the primary school many exceptions exist, e.g. no assessment using grades takes place during the first two years. Instead pupils receive a written report about their general development and achievement.

The individual (mathematics) teacher decides about the ways of marking (system of scaling or setting points, rough description of her criteria, goal- and reference- or average-oriented) and grading at the end of each term, and the final school certificate. Except for the general rules stated by the school laws, there are few controls from the school administration or the head as long as parents do not complain. From each written formal classwork the teacher must choose three examples to show to the head, one representing the best work, one the average and one, the worst, and the head must sign that these have been seen. This is a formality as long as no problem occurs.

In a few states of Germany such as Baden-Württemberg, Bayern, Saarland, different procedures have to be followed with respect to the school leaving certificate. These states have centralised final school examinations in major subjects including mathematics at the end of each school type — a residue of the French occupation in the 19th century. And since the unification of Germany some of the new states tried to continue the old GDR-wide system of final examinations by designing centralised examinations for each single state (i.e. Saxonia, Thuringia, Mecklenburg-Vorpommern).

The marking scheme in mathematics which is seen by teachers as objective, is in fact 'average-oriented', average only referring to the achievement of the class. Attainment of pupils is judged according to the teacher's learning goals, not to standardised external achievement goals. Many mathematics teachers aim at a rough normal distribution in their marking.

The tasks and problems of the written classwork in school mathematics are designed by the mathematics teacher, but mainly taken from either textbooks or teacher-designed material. Classworks require application of mathematical algorithms and standard calculation or transformation. Emphasis is placed on the correctness of solution and presentation. This approach emphasises a view of mathematics which is fragmented into topics that are self-contained by their tasks and concluding tests.

Function of assessment

The principle of teacher-based assessment is fundamental for the German system. Assessment therefore plays a major role in the teacher's teaching design and classroom work in mathematics. In discussing the role of assessment, mathematics teachers refer to several functions of their marking scheme:

— The regular reports provide reliable and valuable information for the parents and pupils about the pupils' level of attainment and about the learning process within a given attainment level of a class (relative marking); the teacher interprets the pupils' attainment as feedback of her teaching success (so-called report function).

— A carefully reported series of grades during the school year offer continuous monitoring of pupils' attainment and the possibility of direct and quick correction through differentiated remedial teaching (control-function).

— Continuous assessment and monitoring is used to control behaviour and raise motivation. Bad grades are not only used as a judgement of lack of knowledge and skills, but also as a disciplinary action.

— Assessment results and grades are seen to have a diagnostic function. A series of grades possibly predict and provide reliable prognoses of school achievement over a period of time[6],

— The most important function of grades is seen in that they seem to offer a rational means for selection. Grades decide who passes to the upper levels or higher types of school and these decisions are seen to be unchallengeable.

Negative aspects are seen in the by-products of the socialisation into such an assessment system. Grading trains pupils in, and accustoms them to, accepting the ethos of the achievement-oriented society, but also often to fail. Instead of developing intrinsic motivation, pupils only learn to achieve good grades and design by-pass strategies to avoid or deal with written classwork and active participation in classroom in an 'economic way'[7].

Empirical surveys on assessment

Although there is an almost complete lack of survey studies or detailed analyses of assessment results, general data suggest that at first glance, girls seem to be privileged by the German assessment system. At least since the educational reform of the 60s facilitated the access to higher secondary education and introduced general co-education, girls seem to have profited more than boys. They mostly start school at age 6 (while boys more often start one year later), they rarely have to repeat, they show fewer learning difficulties which force teachers to call for the help of school psychologists and aides, they have better grades in nearly all school subjects in primary school. More girls than boys access higher secondary schools, more girls than boys get the school leaving examination at upper secondary level, the 'Abitur'. Fewer girls leave school without any certificate, i.e. they are successful in getting their final certificate (Schümer 1985, Backes 1987).

Their average grades in the Abitur would allow more girls than boys to pursue university studies, even those which are restricted in access by 'Numerus Clausus'[8].

If good grades are the only precondition for entering highly demanding vocations or professions, girls would get into them, but fewer girls than boys opt for high achievement courses in mathematics and science in secondary II, fewer girls start studies at university level, particularly in mathematics, science and engineering[9].

Girls usually choose among a very restricted range of few, typically 'female', vocations and professions and they still avoid technologically-oriented vocations. Their success in school does not encourage them to leave traditional 'female' routes.[10]

Assessment results in higher, college-bound secondary mathematics show lower achievement of girls than of boys, compensated for by better grades in languages or other subjects.

Some general findings follow:

Gender differences: large empirical surveys carried out in the 70s and 80s in Austria and (West) Germany showed that girls receive significantly better grades in all school types and year groups except in mathematics and physics, with the highest differences in languages.[11] They generally get better final grades than in single written classworks. Explanations developed in several studies emphasise that girls are better behaved and cause fewer disciplinary problems, they are more industrious.

Differences between different subjects, school types and year groups: empirical studies point out that pupils receive significantly better grades in the fine arts subjects than in the core subjects like mathematics, German literature and foreign languages. Significant differences between different teachers, schools and school types can be detected within behavioural grades due to a high uncertainty about marking industriousness or attention. Studies show that grading in primary schools is usually less severe, and that grading becomes more severe the older the pupil. In particular at the Gymnasium it gets harder and harder to achieve higher grades.

Severe criticism was expressed in the 70s about teacher-based assessment. Studies examined whether teacher-based assessment fulfilled the classical test theory criteria. It was shown that grades were not objective in all subjects including mathematics. Small scale studies showed that teacher-based grades were not reliable or valid and so many educationalists called for the introduction of 'objective' achievement or attainment tests. It is interesting to note however that despite this criticism of teacher-based assessment, further studies in the 80s showed teachers' grades and testing results produced similar figures (Bavaria and Baden-Württemberg compared with North-Rhine-Westphalia, see Roeder et al. 1986). The criticism of grades for pedagogical reasons was more radical and aimed at their total abolition. This debate had some influence in primary schools where grades in the first two years were replaced by reports on the development of the individual pupil.

School mathematics and teacher education

Whereas the primary and Hauptschule teacher traditionally was trained at Pedagogical Academies more as a pedagogue with a poor background in scientific understanding and restricted content knowledge, the mathematics teacher for Gymnasium and Realschule had always been seen as a subject specialist mainly trained at the university as a mathematician, with almost no pedagogical background.

As a result of the educational reform of the 60s, the teacher education system also had to change. A common core mathematics curriculum for all school types and extension of compulsory schooling to age 15 or 16 necessitated a convergence and rapprochement of the different teacher preparation systems. The increased demands on the scientific qualifications of the future teachers, in particular those in the primary and Hauptschule, led to the development of the teacher as subject specialist for all school types. Finally, moves towards establishing comprehensive schools made mathematics education and teacher education a political and economic issue.

By political decisions at the federal level, the teachers of Hauptschule became subject specialists, their education being organised into two phases like the higher secondary teacher training. The academic studies provided by pedagogical academies or institutes were turned into a more theoretical (scientific) phase, now in some states, at universities, too, complemented by a practical phase at the 'Haupt- and Fachseminare' (seminaries for relating general didactics and subject didactics to practical teaching) under the supervision of school administrations and the direction of experienced teachers.

Teacher students for the higher secondary schools, (Realschule and Gymnasium, including technical and vocational colleges) on the other hand, had to pass a greater part of their university studies in the education department. A certain range of knowledge in educational and social sciences, in particular in psychology and pedagogy, and finally in mathematical didactics, too, was required by regulations in some states. Because of these changes, it became possible to discuss a range of assessment modes and practices in pre-service teacher education of all school types. Debates about the adequacy of current practices were also raised in the second phase of teacher training and in in-service education for the first time.

School mathematics and assessment in primary school

Children start compulsory schooling at the age of 6 or 7, while preschool for 5 year-olds is an option which is only taken up by 1% of the age population. During primary schooling, teachers assess on the basis of observation and on written homework and classwork. For 1st and 2nd graders written reports are provided; but starting from grade 3, pupils get regular half yearly reports with grades on behaviour as well as for each subject taught.

In primary school there is a lack of mathematics specialists. Mathematics is mostly taught and assessed by non-mathematics teachers whose background is poor with serious consequences for the method and content of teaching. Mostly female, the teachers often have an ambivalent relationship with mathematics and tend to restrict their teaching to standard arithmetic and traditional calculation of word problems. Except for naming shapes and calculating sizes they do not teach geometry. Beyond textbooks or self-prepared work sheets with exercises they use very few materials. Lip-service is paid to pedagogical principles like open learning, discovery learning or group work, but used by only a few teachers. The focus of assessment in mathematics therefore is traditional arithmetic and social arithmetic.

Many researchers complain that behaviour and social patterns influence the assessment results. Girls often get good grades for behaviour. Their written classwork attracts good grades because it is carefully done and follows the teacher's instructions. The content and method of assessment in primary schools keeps pupils dependent on the teacher. Girls in particular develop their social attitudes in accordance with teachers' attitudes and beliefs, self-concepts and trust in capabilities (Horstkemper 1987, Schümer 19865, Valtin and Warm 1985). Girls rely more on within-class offerings, whereas the boys are additionally challenged by out-of-school activities. Girls, often misused by teachers to create the social climate, lack the criteria for independent self-evaluation. Their good grades in all subjects including mathematics, seem to socialise them into inappropriate behaviours for secondary schooling.

School mathematics and assessment in secondary schools

In most states of the FRG (except Berlin), school choices are made at 10 years. On the basis of teacher recommendations, parents decide to which track of secondary schooling their children will pass, but the children remain on probation in that track for the first half year. It is very difficult to change this early selection even though, officially, it is stated that opportunities for change should exist. If changes occur they are almost always from higher to lower secondary schools. Assessment at the end of primary school is the first most important measure which can determine the future career of pupils.[12]

Until the educational reform of the 60s, only single-sex schools offered higher secondary mathematics education for girls. The expansion of the Gymnasium opened higher secondary schooling for all by introducing general co-education.[13]

Single sex schools are very rare today.

Assessment principles are shaped or determined by the attitudes and beliefs of mathematics teachers towards mathematics and mathematics learning. This is influenced mainly by their teacher education and professional perspective and orientation. The traditional self-concept of the mathematics teacher is as a mathematician and is held by mathematics educators at all levels of the educational system, including teacher training at universities. The teaching staff at secondary level is male-dominated although 30% of students in mathematics are women. The proportion of practising female mathematics teachers is about 10% at Gymnasium and about 15% at the Hauptschule or Realschule, mainly due to the fact that teacher education for secondary school demands two school subjects. The favourite combination in Gymnasium is still mathematics and science, in particular mathematics and physics, so the image of the mathematics teacher held by pupils is shaped by the social image of these two subjects mediated by teaching.

The image of mathematics held by mathematics teachers is often characterised by the belief in the five myths: objectivity, certainty, indubitability, unity and universality of mathematics which, for teaching reasons, can be condensed and fixed as particular tasks. Many teachers follow this Platonist view of mathematics which in consequence is complemented by an understanding of teaching mathematics as transmitting a product in terms of content. In their design of learning opportunities they often refer to biological interpretations of talent and giftedness in mathematics, in particular in the Gymnasium.[14]

In secondary schools, although assessment modes have not changed substantially, girls now achieve higher grades, but they continue to complain about lacking comprehensive and meaningful understanding. They 'resign' from mathematics learning. When girls are assessed in what has been taught (algorithmic procedures, operations and rules) they continue to be successful. When they are assessed in what they have not been explicitly taught, transfer, problem solving, they fail as they have no other experiences of mathematics outside of school. The same performance is interpreted differently by teachers when provided by girls or by boys; girls are simply hard working, boys are creative even when breaking rules and causing chaos (Horstkemper 1987).

The last years of secondary schooling (the upper secondary level) is more differentiated. Pupils have to choose among offerings of basic and high achievement courses which differ in quantity and quality of teaching and content. The organisation of teaching is influenced by the American course system. High achievement courses in mathematics are seen as preconditions for many studies at the university, not only in mathematics and science, although the assessment results in these courses do not strongly influence the average grades in the Abitur. The assessment system changes into more regularly collected grades within another, more differentiated scale of 15 points during the final school years. It remains, however, teacher-based. Negative experiences in mathematics and the lack of encouragement by mathematics teachers are seen as causes for the very small proportion of girls who opt for high achievement courses in mathematics in the final years of secondary schooling (i.e. Brehmer 1989, Sommer 1983).

School mathematics and assessment in Hauptschule — a special case

Mathematics teaching at Hauptschule as well as at comprehensive schools is differentiated into two or three tracks according to the achievement levels of pupils. The overall achievement of girls compared to boys in mathematics in terms of grades seems to be favourable. There are more girls than boys in upper tracks, more girls than boys get their final certificate of Hauptschule which is a precondition for apprenticeship contracts.[15]

More detailed information can be gained from an empirical study which analysed data provided by the centralised examinations at the end of compulsory schooling in Hauptschule in Baden-Württemberg. Girls'achievement in the final exam is lower although they get better grades than boys in the classroom. They fail in particular in social or applied arithmetic, especially when the context does not refer to their own experiences or daily life. Girls did not work on certain tasks given in the exam, in particular those about speed and technical themes, and geometry (calculation of angles). Very often they chose the wrong approach to word problems whereas boys are more successful in these. The authors interpret their results as follows:

> The results seem to suggest the conclusion that teachers (at Hauptschule in BW) concentrate on arithmetic and applied arithmetic which leads to considerable success for pupils...Themes from Algebra and Geometry seem to be neglected which leads to failure among low achieving pupils. Girls had special difficulties in applied arithmetic and geometry which they avoided because of lack of self-esteem. The changed assessment scale in the last examination which put more emphasis on word problems and geometry, disadvantaged girls particularly. (Berger et al. 1992, pp.77ff, translation by the authors)

Proposals to improve the situation

Several proposals have been made in the last few years to improve the assessment mode in German schools. The most important are:

— to include discussion of assessment modes and practices in both pre-service and in-service teacher education. The exchange of ideas on a range of assessment modes, and the evidence they might supply, could only enhance practice;

— to use standardised tests from time to time in order to compare the results of teacher's own assessments, with general results based on external criteria. Additionally, the development of informal tests, perhaps criterion-referenced, would provide feedback on the results of teaching without the pressure of grading. Educationalists are demanding the separation of evaluation from grading, instead of the current mix. Such a separation could relieve the pressure and anxiety observed in classrooms at present;

— that teachers should stipulate in advance how they will assess and the criteria they will use. The assessment results should be reported not only in grades, but also in a verbal statement. As already indicated, this style is used in the first two years of primary school as well as in a few independent schools;

— to develop richer and broader models of assessment in order to overcome the restricted task orientation. Examples such as coursework, now common in English schools, have been proposed. A wider range of assessment styles could focus on process as well as product, promoting problem-solving activities and encouraging the development of student profiles instead of single assessments at a fixed point in time.

These proposals are currently debated amongst didacticians but are not yet the subject of debate amongst experienced teachers responsible for the second practical phase of teacher education. Neither are they yet the subject of political or administrative decisions.

Assessment and teacher pre-service and in-service training in the unified Germany

The unification of Germany has challenged the system of the old FRG. The integration of the two different systems raised debates about assessment, teacher education and role of schooling. Important problems in teacher education which could change the narrow understanding of teaching and assessing in school mathematics have been identified.

— *Relating theory to practice and integrating the different parts of training* describes an urgent problem of teacher education. There is a lack of successful attempts to integrate didactics and mathematics, connect the various subjects of the studies to create comprehensive approaches, and provide designs for project work and co-operative teaching. This, taken with the lack of co-operation and relations between the two phases of teacher education has resulted in teachers becoming overburdened and has pushed them into ritualised and unquestioning teaching practices. It has made them hostile towards practical innovations or applications of research findings. It causes a lack of motivation and introduces distrust into the professional perspective of the teachers.

— *The mathematical education* provided by university mathematicians through traditional lectures and the requirement to solve compartmentalised exercises only, with no emphasis on reflection and metalevel-thinking, often leads to Platonic views of, and attitudes towards, mathematics which do not foster new and differentiated ways of teaching mathematics *to all pupils*.

— *The engineering approach to mathematics teaching* tends to reduce mathematical didactics to an execution and realisation of administrative regulations and curricular programmes. The search for 'teacher-proof' curricula or 'teacher-proof' textbooks reinforces traditional prescriptive and normative teaching ideals and the illusion of best means and methods for any pupils or purposes. Guiding pupils to a social construction of knowledge and social negotiation of meaning through new teaching paradigms then becomes a utopia.

— Administrative measures designed to regulate the increasing number of teacher candidates has led to a changed role for the expert teachers in the seminaries of the second phase. The teacher trainers have to take on more tasks in evaluating and assessing in addition to observing, advising, consulting, and teaching. The function of being more selective has changed the co-operative atmosphere in the seminaries into one which is competitive, discouraging, and anxiety-creating.

— The political problem of whether to refer to a *surplus of trained teachers* or a *shortage of posts for teachers* finally focuses on the question: *Do we need more teachers of mathematics* or, more important, *what are the needs and goals of mathematics education?* Changing regulations and turning the 'screw of examinations', together with restriction of posts, aim at hindering access to the profession. A shortage of teachers of mathematics (subject matter specialists) in the early 1970s was followed by a surplus of trained teachers in the 1990s. This has led to an ageing teacher population with its associated problems of conservatism and resistance to change.

Similar to the use of law against the medical profession in some countries, the assessment system has been an increasing focus of challenge by parents and pupils. This has resulted in a tightening of regulations and a closure against pedagogical innovation. Despite the apparent variety within the states, the imposition of unanimity has created a system which is large, heavy, and lumbering. The assessment style typifies this system, is not questioned, and fails to take account of its impact nor to look for convincing alternatives.

References

1. When discussing the German system we only speak about the system of the old states of the FRG although this system will apply in the future to the old GDR. The educational system of the GDR was completely different in several respects; a centralised unified programme for a 10 year comprehensive school and an additional 2 year higher secondary school, intermittent centralised examinations, one single textbook series for all pupils, different styles of preservice teacher education (see Keitel 1993).

2. The exception is the state of Berlin where British influence resulted in a pattern of 6 years primary and 4 years compulsory secondary schooling.

3. The Gymnasium maintains a strict academic orientation despite the fact that many pupils with Abitur now enter practical careers such as banking or management.

4. A few attempts are made to integrate, for example, physically handicapped or mentally retarded pupils into the regular primary school. Many parents tried through the legal system to have their 'sorted out' children placed in ordinary schools. Nonetheless there are about 3.7-4.2% of the whole school population in special needs schools!

5. In the upper secondary level significantly fewer written classworks have to be done, i.e. 4 per year of 3-6 lessons duration depending on the subject and the year group.

6. This belief of teachers seems to be justified by empirical studies: A sociological (longitudinal) study which analysed the educational and professional success of about 5000 men and women gave evidence that the teachers' evaluation and assessment as a general aptitude measure for results of schooling have validity and reliability (Sommer 1983), but also demands careful analysis of why pupils have got their bad grades and for what deficiencies.

7. An inquiry of pupils from HS and Gymnasium offered data concerning the attitude of pupils to the system of grades: all pupils have a close relationship to the system of grading, and feel very dependent on grades; they create a close connection between level of achievement and social status which increases with age. However, as pupils generally do not accept the system of grades as a valid and reliable instrument of measuring they are unable to develop a reliable self-estimation of their capabilities after school (Seewald 1983). Performance and competition as norms of action and interaction in the school are directly experienced by pupils, and the openly powerful position of the teacher and its consequences for the teaching and learning situation create additional problems for assessment (Ulich 1983, Weiss 1989).

8. 'Numerus clausus' means that universities offer access to a restricted number of students only in some subjects like medicine, pharmacy, psychology etc; selection is done by either grades in final certificates, tests or random choice.

9. Among the students of all universities in Germany in 1990 there were 31.5% female students in mathematics, 10% in physics, 15% in computer science, 12.3% in engineering, 3.3% in electrotechnics, 39.8% in architecture, 53.5% in biology, 68.6% in pharmacy; on university staff, female professors in mathematics and science 2%, female scientific co-workers in mathematics and science 16.2%

10. Special reference must be made to the teaching profession. 79% of all primary teachers are women; more women are employed part-time in all school types

(30-50%) (Valtin Warm, 1985, p.7); managing or leading positions however are taken by men: the proportion of women in headteacher positions varies between 8% in Baden- Württemberg to 23% in Berlin. On average there are 15% female heads in primary schools (Ibid, p.167). Besides female teachers, mothers have the greatest influence on schools: compared with most other countries the German school is mainly half-day, with no generally regulated schooling time. Mothers are responsible for tasks related to schooling (buying of materials for school, organisation of the daily time-schedule, help with homework, compensation for cancelled or dropped lessons, etc.). The German school system only functions because of a high proportion of unpaid private co-working of mothers, in particular with respect to homework-control. Mothers are obliged to supervise, motivate, and support their children's school success. In primary schools they actively participate in instruction, in excursions, organising and designing school parties, etc. The conception of 'open schools' is mainly based on implicitly demanded, unpaid, co-operation of mothers (Enders-Drangässer 1990, Portmann 1985)

11. See e.g. the survey of Knoche (1969) in which the reports of 14000 students were examined or of Karas (1978).

12. Some studies have shown that teacher recommendations at the end of primary are highly biased by gender, social class and ethnic origin, and that the teachers' recommendations more strongly influence choices of lower class parents than of middle or upper class parents, a fact which was not changed by the educational reform (Hansen, Roesner, Weissbach 1986). By contrast, however, an examination of the relation between teachers' recommendations to higher secondary tracks and future pupil success at school showed that teachers are just and distribute pupils into school types in a reasonable way. (Bott and Merkens 1985).

13. A critical analysis of the expansion of higher secondary schools in the context of examining school achievement quotes heads of Gymnasia asserting that the level of attainment of pupils has dramatically decreased because of the opening of this school type to 'everybody' (Roeder, Baumert, Sang, Schmitz 1986).

14. Inquiries among pupils shows a depressing image of mathematics teachers. They are described as often impersonal, using their power because of the objectivity of mathematics, but nevertheless sticking to prejudices (girls are not gifted in maths). Their reference to the systematic and linear sequence of mathematical topics in lessons appears mostly as a fiction. Pupils see themselves more unconnectedly and meaninglessly working in a 'quarry' than following a logical or psychological order (Andelfinger and Voigt 1984, Andelfinger 1990)

15. Statements from girls show that they have difficulty in entering non-traditional vocations, they experience pressure when choosing 'male' jobs, and girls between 15 and 19 years have to struggle to obtain apprenticeship contracts. (Seidenspinner and Burger 1984).

Bibliography

Andelfinger, B., Voigt, J.: (1984) *Der Alltag des Mathematikunterrichts und die Ausbildung von Referendaren.* (The daily life of mathematics classroom and the education of teacher students in the second phase). Occasional Paper 51. Institut für Didaktik der Mathematik, Universität Bielefeld.

Andelfinger, B.: 1990a, *Wir wollten alles besser machen. Eindrücke aus einer Befragung zum Analysisunterricht und Vorschläge zur Sekundarstufel.* (We wanted to do better. Impressions from an inquiry about teaching calculus). Landesinstitut für Schule und Weiterbildung, Soest.

Anonym: 1982, 'Lehrerbedarf: Studieren für die Arbeitslosigkeit' (The need for teachers: training for unemployment), *Uni Journal,* 6 (9), 16-22.

Backes, G.: 1987, Frauen im Saarländischen Bildungssystem. (Women in the educational system of Saarland) in: *Statistische Nachrichten,* 3, 11-35

Bartnitzky, H., Portmann, R. (eds.): 1992, *Leistung der Schule —Leistung der Kinder.* (Achievement of the school — achievement of the pupils) Beiträge zur Reform der Grundschule 87, Arbeitskreis Grundschule, Frankfurt a.M.

Berger, R. Gerster, H.D., Lörcher, G.A., Rümmele, H.: 1992, *Mathematikkenntnisse in der Abschlußprüfung an Hauptschulen Baden-Württemberg 1988.* Eine empirische Untersuchung zu Schülerfehlern und Lösungsverfahren. (Mathematical knowledge in the final examination at modern schools in Baden-Württemberg 1988). PH Freiburg, Freiburg.

Brehmer, I.: 1989, *Mädchen, Macht (und) Mathe.* Geschlechtsspezifische Leistungskurswahl in der reformierten Oberstufe. (Gender specific choice of high achievement course in the reformed secondary II). Die Landesregierung NRW, Düsseldorf.

Bott, P., Merkens, H.: 1985, *Schulverlaufsuntersuchungen.* (The course of study in schools) Zwischenbericht des Forschungsprojektes. Freie Universität Berlin, Berlin.

BMBW (Bundesminister für Bildung und Wissenschaft) (eds.): 1991, *Aktuell. Bildung und Wissenschaft: Studenten an Hochschulen 1975 bis 1990.* Referat für Presse und Öffentlichkeit, Bonn.

Damerow, P.: 1977, *Die Reform des Mathematikunterrichts in der Sekundarstufe.* (The reform of mathematics education in secondary I) Band 1: Reformziele, Lehrpläne, Klett, Stuttgart.

Dohse, W.: 1963, *Das Schulzeugnis.* (The school report-certificate) Beltz, Weinheim.

Enders-Drangässer, U., Fuchs, C.: 1989, *Interaktionen der Geschlechter. Sexismusstrukturen in der Schule* (Interaction of genders. Sexist structures in school). Juventa, Weinheim.

Furck, C.L.: 1972, *Das pädagogische Problem der Leistung in der Schule.* (The pedagogical problem of assessing achievement in our schools) Beltz, Weinheim.

Hansen, R., Roesner, E., Weissbach, B. 1986, Der Übergang in die Sekundarstufe I. (The transition to the secondary school) *Jahrbuch der Schulentwicklung,* 4, 70-101.

Hohenzollern, J.G., Liedtcke, M. (eds.): 1991, Schülerbeurteilung und Schulzeugnisse. (Pupils' evaluation and the school reports-certificates) Klinkhardt, Bad Heilbrunn.

Horstkemper, M.: 1987, Schule, *Geschlecht und Selbstvertrauen.* Eine Längsschnittstudie über Mädchensozialisation in der Schule. (School, gender and selfconfidence. A longitudinal study on socialisation of girls in school). Beltz, Weinheim.

Hopf, D.: 1980, *Der Mathematikunterricht. Eine empirische Untersuchung zur Didaktik und Unterrichtsmethode in der 7. Klasse des Gymnasiums,* (Mathematics instruction, an empirical investigation of didactics and methodology in 7th grade Gymnasium) Klett, Stuttgart.

Howson, G., Keitel, C., Kilpatrick, J.: 1981, Curriculum Development in Mathematics. Cambridge University Press, Cambridge.

Karas, E.: 1978, Leistungsbeurteilung an allgemeinbildenden Höheren Schulen (Assessment in general higher education), Teubner, Wien.

Kaiser-Messmer, G.: 1992, Mädchen und Mathematik — Wo liegen die Probleme? (Girls and mathematics — where are the problems?) in: 5-10 *Schulmagazin* 2, 8-11.

Keitel, C.: 1980, 'Entwicklungen im Mathematikunterricht'. (Developments in mathematics instruction) In: Max-Planck-Institut für Bildungsforschung/Projekgruppe Bildungsbericht (Hg.) *Bildung in der Bundesrepublik Deutschland. Daten und Analysen.* Bd. 1: Entwicklungen seit 1950, Klett, Stuttgart, 447-500.

Keitel, C.: 1986, Social Needs and Secondary Mathematics Education. In: *For the Learning of Mathematics,* 6, 3, p.27-33.

Keitel, C.: 1990, Mädchen und Mathematik. (Girls and mathematics) In: *Mathematica Didactica,* 13, 3/4, p. 31-46.

Keitel, C.: 1992, The Education of Teachers of Mathematics — An Overview. In: Blum et. al. (eds.): Mathematics Education in the Federal Republic of Germany. *Zentralblatt für Didaktik der Mathematik,* Sonderausgabe/Special Issue, 1992.

Keitel, C.: 1993, Notes on the unification of the two German states and the integration of two different educational systems. In: *The Curriculum Journal,* 4, 1, 131-135.

Knoche, W.: 1969, Jungen, Mädchen, Lehrer und Schüler im Zensurenvergleich. Eine Untersuchung an 14000 Schülern aus 50 Gymnasien. (Boys, girls, teachers and pupils compared by grades). Beltz, Weinheim.

Kühn, R.: 1983, Bedingungen für Schulerfolg. *Zusammenhänge zwischen Schülermerkmalen, häuslicher Umwelt und Schulnoten.* (Conditions for success in school, relationship between pupils' characterisitics, family environment and school, grades) Göttingen.

Pfister, G., Valtin, R. (eds.): 1993, *MädchenStärken. Probleme der Koedukation in der Grundschule.* (Empowering girls/power of girls. Problems of coeducation in primary school) Beiträge zur Reform der Grundschule 90, Arbeitskreis Grundschule, Frankfurt a.M.

Portmann, R.: 1985, Lehrerinnen und Mütter — Erfahrungen mit den Schwierigkeiten einer Beziehung. In: Valtin, R., Warm, U. (eds.): 1985, *Frauen machen Schule. Probleme von Mädchen und Lehrerinnen in der Grundschule.* (Women make school. Problems of girls and female teachers in primary school) Arbeitskreis Grundschule, Frankfurt a.M., 202-215.

Prengel, A.: 1984, Schulversagerinnen. *Versuch über diskursive, sozialhistorische und pädagogische Ausgrenzungen des Weiblichen.* (Female school failing) Focus, Gießen.

Roeder, P.M., Baumert, J., Sang, F., Schmitz, B.: 1986, Expansion des Gymnasiums und Leistungsentwicklung. (Expansion of Gymnasium and standards of achievement) in: *Zeitschrift für Soziologie*, 3, 15, 210-220.

Rösner, E.: (1989) Abschied von der Hauptschule (Dismission of the modern school) Fischer, Frankfurt a.M.

Schmidt, G., Silkenbeumer, E.: 1983, Zensurenlose Zeugnisse. Zur Produktion abweichenden Verhaltens in der Grundschule. (School reports without grades. About the production of deviant behaviour in primary schools) in: Kury, H., Lerchenmüller, H. (eds.): *Schule, psychische Probleme und sozialabweichendes Verhalten*, 187-221. Heymanns, Köln.

Schümer, G.: 1985, Geschlechtsunterschiede im Schulerfolg — Auswertung statistischer Daten (Gender differences in success in schools — results from statistical data). In: Valtin, R., Warm, U. (eds.) 1985, Frauen machen Schule. *Probleme von Mädchen und Lehrerinnen in der Grundschule* (Women make school = 'women become the accepted'. Problems of girls and female teachers in primary school). Arbeitskreis Grundschule, Frankfurt a.M., 95- 100.

Seewald, C.: 1983, *Leistungsentwicklung und Selbstverständnis von Schülern.* (The development of achievement and self-concept of pupils) Diss. Universität Bielefeld, Bielefeld.

Seidenspinner, G., Burger, A.: 1984, *Gute Noten sind kein Schlüssel zum Arbeitsmarkt.* (Good grades do not guarantee access to the labor market) Vom Nutzen weiblicher Lohnarbeit. Alltag und Biografien von Mädchen, 3, 11-44, Leske und Budrich, Opladen

Sommer, W.: 1983, *Bewährung des Lehrerurteils.* Eine empirische Untersuchung über den Aussagewert des Lehrerurteils für den Bildungs- und Berufserfolg. (Validation and reliability of teacher assessment. An empirical study on the predicting value of teacher assessment for success in education and vocation) Klinkhardt, Bad Heilbrunn.

Statistisches Bundesamt (eds.): 1993, *Bildung und Kultur.* (Education and culture) Fachserie 11, Reihe 1, Allgemeinbildende Schulen. Metzler/Poeschel, Stuttgart.

Ulich, K.: 1983, *Schüler und Lehrer im Schulalltag* (Pupil and teacher in daily life of the school) Eine Sozialpsychologie der Schule. Beltz, Weinhein.

Valtin, R., Warm, U. (eds.): 1985, *Frauen machen Schule. Probleme von Mädchen und Lehrerinnen in der Grundschule.* (Women make school = 'women become the accepted'. Problems of girls and female teachers in primary school). Arbeitskreis Grundschule, Frankfurt a.M.

Weiss, R.: 1989, *Leistungsbeurteilung in den Schulen — Notwendigkeit oder Übel?* (Assessment in schools — necessity or troublemaker?) Jugend und Volk, Wien.

CHAPTER SIX

The Republic of Ireland

Kathleen Lynch
Sean Close
Elizabeth Oldham

Introduction

The purpose of this chapter is to examine gender differences in assessment procedures and in performance in mathematics in the Republic of Ireland; the principal focus is on first and second-level education. It opens with a short description of Irish education and outlines briefly some of the major gender differences which characterise the system. Having set the context within which mathematics education takes place, we go on to examine curriculum provision patterns and take-up rates in the field of mathematics with specific reference to gender. Using data from national examinations, and both national and international surveys, we focus on performance differences in mathematics. Specific attention is given to differences across content areas and cognitive categories. The relationship between gender differences and styles of assessment is also discussed and we conclude with a brief analysis of the context within which debates about assessment in mathematics is currently taking place in Ireland.

The Education System: General Characteristics and Gender Differences

Formal education in the Republic of Ireland takes place in three separate phases. Primary education begins at age 4 and continues for a minimum of 8 years until age 12. At the age of 12 all pupils are entitled to enter the second-level system, although pupils may be over age 12 on leaving primary education. Attendance at formal education is compulsory up to the age of 15 years. Second-level education is typically of five years duration, roughly from age 12-13 to age 17-18. (Some schools provide a six year cycle; such a cycle is being introduced for all students in 1994). At age 17, pupils who are suitably qualified may enter third-level education (i.e. the universities and other institutes of higher education). Approximately 73% of those who enter second level complete the senior cycle; in addition, almost 40% of the age cohort go on to higher education (Department of Education, 1992:45, 183).

The position of girls and young women in Irish education is a somewhat contradictory one. On the one hand, girls have attained higher aggregate grades in major public examinations than boys (Greaney and Kellaghan 1984:180; Clancy, 1987:13) and are more likely than boys to complete second-level education (in 1989/90, for example, 55.2% of the 17 and 18 year olds in second-level education were girls, (Department of Education,1991:Tables 3.2, 3.3). On the other hand, men slightly outnumber women in third-level education (Table 1, page 115) although the differences here are declining. Indeed, Clancy (1989:1) predicts that if the present growth rates in women's participation continue, they will shortly constitute a majority of new entrants to higher education.

Men greatly outnumber women, however, in the increasingly expanding technological sectors of higher education (Clancy 1988:17-18). In 1988, for example, only 15% of the entrants to engineering courses in the university sector of higher education were women , while the comparable rate of entry in the other, mostly technological, colleges was 6.5% (ibid). While this represents an improvement from the mid-1970s when only 5.1% of new university entrants to engineering were women (HEA, 1975/76) women's participation in the technological sector had not changed between 1980 and 1986 (Clancy, 1988:73). This is true despite the increased participation and achievement of girls in mathematics and the sciences over the same period. Given that the proportion of women

114

Table 1: Female/Male Participation Rates at the 3 Major Education Levels				
	Females		Males	
	N	%	N	%
First Level 4-12 years (approx)	272,592	48.6	288,278	51.4
Second Level 12-7/18years (aaprox)	174,872	51.1	167,492	48.9
Third Level 17-18 years + approx	30,738	46.6	35,211	53.4
TOTAL	478,202	-	490,981	-
Source: Department of Education (1991) Statistical Report, 1989/90, Table 1.				

entering the science faculties in the universities is now almost equal to that of men at 48%, this would seem to indicate that girls do not lack competence in technologically-related subjects, rather they 'choose' not to enter the technological field for a variety of reasons (WITS,1991). What they 'choose' instead is to enter fields such as teacher education, the humanities and the social sciences (Clancy, 1988).

Patterns of Control, and Differences in Types of School Attended

Figure 1 (see page 116) gives an overview of the overall structure and control of the formal education system in the Republic of Ireland. From this one can see that almost all Irish primary school children attend publicly funded national schools. These are with a few exceptions, denominationally managed schools (mostly by the Roman Catholic authorities). At second level, denominational education persists, particularly in the dominant secondary sector (64% of all pupils are in the secondary sector).

Not only is there a strong tradition of denominational education in Ireland, there is also a strong tradition of single sex education: 47% of all pupils at second level are in single sex schools and almost 40% of those in primary are in either totally, or mostly single sex schools (i.e. with co-education in infant classes only) (Table II, page 117).

Figure 1: Irish Education: Structure of the formal system

Level	Primary (compulsory)	Second Level (compulsory up to age 15)	Third Level
Duration	8 Years	5 or 6 Years	3 or 4 years for basic degree
Age of Pupils/students	4-12 years	12-17/18 years	17/18 years at entry
Control and Type	National schools jointly owned by Church and State; all but 10 are denominationally managed; 98.1% of all primary schools are state aided	Secondary: privately owned and controlled but state aided (63.8% of 2nd level pupils) Vocational: entirely state owned and controlled (24.6% of pupils) Community: jointly owned by the state and R.C. religious order. Comprehensive: owned by the state and controlled by the state and religious representatives (C. and C. combined — 11.6% of pupils)	All State Aided Universities, Colleges of Education, Colleges of Technology, Regional Technical Colleges, Art Colleges.
Examinations	No formal examination but records are kept of a pupil's performance over his/her primary career	Junior Certificate* (after 3 years) Leaving Certificate (at the end of 2nd level)	Variety of degrees and diplomas
Fee/Non-Fee	No fees in 98.1%	no fees in 92.7%	All fee paying but grants for low income students

* The Junior Certificate has replaced the Intermediate Certificate for students starting the programme from 1989 onwards.

Table II: Distribution of Pupils between Single Sex and Co-educational Schools at First and Second Level				
	1st Level		2nd Level	
Type of School	N	%	N	%
Co-educational	337,923	60.5	181,129	53.4
Single Sex	145,108	28.1	158,003	46.6
Single Sex but has co-education in some junior classes	57,541	11.4	Not Applicable	
TOTAL	540,572	100.0	339,132	100.0
Source: Department of Education, *Statistical Report,,* 1989/90: Table 6, p.15 and Table 6, p.38.				

Girls are, however, more likely than boys to attend single sex schools at second level — 52% of all girls in second level are in single sex schools compared with 41% of boys (Department of Education, 1991:38, Table 6). This difference reflects a parental preference for single sex education for adolescent girls, as Irish parents are free — within the limits of their income — to send their children to the school of their choice. There are no real gender differences in co-educational participation at the primary level. Girls are also more likely than boys to attend 'secondary' schools, which are the least technically oriented schools in terms of curricula: 69.7% of all girls at second level are in secondary schools compared with 57.6% of boys (Lynch,1991:120).

Curricular Options: The Place of Mathematics

The Historical Context

The place of mathematics in Irish education is strongly influenced by its origins in the nineteenth century. State intervention in education dates from 1831 when the first 'national' (primary schools) were opened. These provided basic education in various subjects including arithmetic and, in some cases, in other branches of mathematics. While girls and boys tended to pursue a common course for the three most junior classes, boys were offered a more demanding course (including some geometry) in the three remaining classes. Similar variations were found in the training programmes for female and male teachers in the national schools. Gender

117

differentiation in the mathematics programmes of primary schools conti-nued, in modified form, up to the end of the 1960s (McGuinness and Oldham, 1982:96). In the 1960s, for example, algebra and geometry were taught in some schools, but were not obligatory in the smaller schools or in classes taught by women (ibid). It was only with the introduction of a new primary curriculum in 1971 that a 'modern and integrated mathema-tics course' was taught to, and by, both sexes (ibid).

A similar pattern of evolution is evident in the second level system. The regulations emanating from the Intermediate Education (Ireland) Act of 1878 'allowed girls (but not boys) to obtain a pass in mathematics by passing algebra alone; later, boys had to offer a mathematical subject in the examination, whereas girls did not' (Tansey, 1978:219 cited by McGuinness and Oldham, 1982). After the foundation of the new state, matters changed very little, except that an 'Elementary Mathematics' course was introduced in the Intermediate Certificate Examination (age 15 approx.) which was open to girls only; also, boys had to pass mathe-matics to obtain their Intermediate Certificate, whereas girls were not even required to present the subject at the examination (Tansey, 1978: 221-228 cited in McGuinness and Oldham, 1982). It is only since 1969 that there has been no formal differences in the type of mathematics courses offered to girls and boys in secondary schools.

There are a variety of historical reasons why girls were offered different syllabi in mathematics over the years. These would include the influence of a strongly patriarchal culture (both within Ireland, and in Britain which ruled all of Ireland up to the early 1920s) and the influence of the Roman Catholic Church which always espoused traditional roles for women as homemakers in marriage. The pursuit of mathematics was not seen to be in accordance with this latter principle as annual reports of the Conference of Convent Secondary Schools (which controlled most of the secondary schools which Irish girls attended) show (Tansey,1978). The changes which have occurred since the late 1960s are the result of a variety of socio-economic changes in the position of women and in society gener-ally. The very schools which offered low grade mathematics courses to girls from the 1920s to the 1950s are now offering the highest grade mathematics courses to girls at all levels (Department of Education,1991).

Primary Curriculum

Since 1971 all Irish pupils have pursued the same curriculum at primary level: this comprises Irish, English, mathematics, social and environmental studies, arts and crafts, music, physical education and religion. This is not to suggest that boys and girls have identical educational experiences. Although no major published research has yet been undertaken on pupils' experiences in primary schools, (such as research on classroom interaction or teacher behaviour) evidence from other countries would suggest that gender differences are likely to be common at the classroom level (Council of Europe 1982; Marland, 1983; Stanworth, 1983; Wilson, 1991). Evidence from the *Teacher's Handbook* for Primary Teachers (1971) certainly indicates that sexism is still alive and well in the official guidelines given to teachers. With regard to the teaching of music the Handbook suggests that:

> While a large number of songs are suited to both boys and girls, some songs are particularly suited to boys: martial, gay, humorous, rhythmic airs. Others are more suited to girls e.g. lullabies, spinning songs, songs tender in content and expression. (ibid:213).

Evidence of sexism is also clearly in evidence in the section dealing with physical education. In senior primary classes the Handbook suggests that:

> ...separate training in movement training may be made for boys and girls. Boys can now acquire a wide variety of skills and techniques and girls often become more aware of style and grace (ibid:310).

While there is a commitment to eliminate these gross examples of sexism from teaching guidelines, and while primary textbooks have been revised for similar reasons, there is little doubt but that much needs to be done to introduce gender equality into the primary system.

The Provision of Subjects on the Curriculum of Second-Level Schools

At second level, pupils pursue a core curriculum (usually for three years) up to the completion of the Junior Certificate examination, at the age of approximately 15 years. The average student takes about eight subjects. The core subjects for a given student vary slightly with school type. Irish,

English and mathematics are compulsory Junior Certificate Subjects, in all types of second-level schools; in addition, history and geography are compulsory in secondary schools plus two other subjects from the approved list of subjects. In community, comprehensive and vocational schools, students can take either art, commerce, mechanical drawing or home economics (in conjunction with Irish, English and mathematics) plus two other subjects from the prescribed list. One can see therefore that mathematics is compulsory for all students up to age 15. It can be taken at three levels, higher, ordinary and foundation (similar gradations also exist in Irish and English).

The senior cycle has been of two years duration although it is now being extended to three years. The Leaving Certificate Examination is taken by most students at the end of senior cycle. There are 31 approved subjects and each of these is offered at a higher and ordinary level. In the case of mathematics, however, there are three syllabi, 'higher', 'ordinary' and 'ordinary alternative'; the latter represents an attempt to develop an alternative to the more traditional mathematics offered in the other two courses. Irish is the only course of study which is compulsory for the Leaving Certificate. One can see therefore that mathematics is not a compulsory subject; this is true for both girls and boys. However, as students take seven subjects on average for the Leaving Certificate, mathematics is taken by almost all students (see section on take-up below).

In general however, schools and pupils do have considerable latitude in their choice of subjects, depending especially on the size of the school. Not only do schools have a choice about what subjects to offer and at which level they offer them, they also exercise a high level of autonomy in internal matters including timetabling (Hannan et al., 1983). They are free to offer a subject only to one particular sex if they so wish and many still do.

The freedom given to schools in curriculum provision and timetabling, especially at senior level, has resulted in very noticeable gender differences in both the availability and take up of particular subjects. As Tables A1 and A2 (Appendix) show, technical subjects (such as mechanical drawing and woodwork at junior level and technical drawing, engineering and construction studies at senior level) are rarely available as options for girls; single sex girls' schools do not offer these subjects generally, while

Table III: Proportion of Single Sex Schools.Offering Particular Subjects to Leaving Certificate Pupils in 1980/81 and in 1989/90

	Girl's Schools		Boy's Schools	
	1980-81	1989-90	1980-81	1989-90
	%	%	%	%
Mathematics (Higher)	73.9	89.4	91.7	90.7
Physics	34.8	78.8	79.2	92.6
Chemistry	73.9	88.9	83.3	87.0
Biology	100.0	97.7	75.0	87.7
History	95.7	97.4	84.0	92.0
Technical Drawing	0.0	3.2	33.3	62.3
Home Economics (Scientific and Social)	95.7	97.4	4.2	19.1
No. of Schools	N/A*	97.4	N/A	162
*N/A means not available				

Sources: The 1980/81 figures are taken from D. Hannan et al.,*Schooling and Sex Roles*, Dublin: Economic and Social Research Institute, 1983, Table 5.7. The 1989/90 figures are taken from the Department of Education (1991) *Statistical Report 1989/90* Table 14.9, p.52.

timetabling in co-educational schools often means that many girls are excluded. Boys, on the other hand, are rarely given the option of doing home economics at either junior or senior level.

In terms of subject provision, gender differences in the sciences and mathematics have been reduced considerably in recent years although they are still significant. As can be seen from Table III above, 89.4% of girls' schools offered higher course mathematics at Leaving Certificate level in 1988/89 and 78.8% offered physics compared with 73.9% and 34.8% offering higher Mathematics and Physics respectively in 1980-81.

The proportion of girls' schools offering physics has more than doubled therefore in the last 10 years, while the proportion offering higher mathematics is now almost equal to that of boys' schools. Indeed, the proportion of girls' schools now offering chemistry (88.9%)and Ordinary mathematics (95.2%) is slightly higher than that of boys' schools where the comparable figures are 87% and 93.2% respectively. Within co-educational schools also, most schools now offer the sciences and mathematics equally to both sexes (Tables A1 and A2).

In terms of formal provision therefore, mathematics is universally available to girls in Irish primary and second-level schools. However, focusing on the *provision* of mathematics does not give the complete picture. When we examine take-up rates, performance and attitudes towards mathematics a more complicated, and less favourable picture emerges for girls.

Take-Up Rates in Second-Level Subjects

Of the students taking the Leaving Certificate, almost all (99% in 1991) take mathematics (NCCA, 1992). As three quarters (approximately) of the age cohort sits for the Leaving Certificate, the rate of take-up of academic mathematics is very high by international standards, it needs some explanation. First, there is the fact that the Leaving Certificate is a general rather than a specialised end-of-school examination. There is no tradition of early specialisation; rather the assumption has been that it is better to keep students' options open as long as possible. A general rather than a specialised programme allows for this. Second, until very recently one was required to pass in five subjects to get one's Leaving Certificate. While the strict Pass:Fail distinction has been dropped, the regulations still specify that students take at least five subjects for the Leaving Certificate Examination. In addition, most higher education institutions and other post-leaving certificate programmes work on the assumption that students will have taken a minimum of five subjects. Also, 'points' (grade point averages) for entry to higher education institutions are calculated on the basis of one's performance per subject, so that having more subjects increases one's chances of gaining points. Points are calculated on one's best six subjects. The reason why mathematics tends to be chosen *per se*, is largely because of its 'market' value. There are a very limited number of courses which one can take in higher education without mathematics (at present, almost two thirds of the places in higher education are in the scientific, technological and business fields, (Clancy, 1988) and all of these require at least ordinary if not higher mathematics). In addition, entry to other careers, such as primary teaching and nursing, is dependent on having attained a reasonable standard in ordinary level mathematics in the Leaving Certificate. Indeed there are many jobs for which higher education is not required but where a reasonable grade in ordinary level Leaving Certificate mathematics is required.

There are gender differences, however, in take-up rates in mathematics. Although a slightly higher proportion of girls than boys take the higher course (A) in mathematics in the junior cycle of second level schools (44% compared with 42% in 1989/90) a noticeably higher proportion of boys (26.1%) than girls (15%) study the higher course in mathematics at the senior level (Table IV). Even those girls who perform as well as boys in Junior Level mathematics do not opt for Higher Course mathematics at the same rate as boys (Hannan et al., 1983:290).

Table IV: Gender Differences in Take-up Rates in Mathematics:Proportion of gender group taking each subject

Course	1989/90*	
	Girls	Boys
	1989/90	1989/90
Intermediate	%	%
Mathematics A (higher)	44.4	42.1
Mathematics B (lower)	43.1	46.5
Mathematics C (lowest)	12.4	11.1
Leaving Certificate (end of second level)		
Mathematics (higher)	15.0	26.1
Mathematics (ordinary)	77.1	65.3
Mathematics (combined course)	6.3	6.7

Source: *Department of Education (1991) Statistical Report 1989/90.* Tables 15.5 and 15.9.

* The take-up rates for all subjects in 1989/90 are presented in the Appendix, Tables A3 and A4.

It seems that the gender difference in take-up in higher mathematics is related to differences in attitudes towards mathematics and the perceived career/job choices which they offer. Research based on a national sample of second-level students found that 'girls have, on average, less positive attitudes than boys to Maths — even at the higher levels of performance.' (Hannan et al. 1983:317). However, data from the follow-up study to the Second International Mathematics Survey (SIMS) undertaken in 1985/86 does not support Hannan's findings. It found that first year girls in second-level schools had a more positive attitude towards mathematics than boys, although the differences were not significant (Carey, 1990:172). Carey points out that the differences here may be due to the differences in the sample (Hannan's study covered intermediate, group and leaving certificate students unlike the follow-up to SIMS which was based only on first year students). However, it would also seem likely that the differences in attitudes can be accounted for in terms of the scales used. The Hannan (1983) study only employed one scale, measuring attitudes towards mathematics. The scale (MATHLIT) assessed the respondents preference for mathematics and science as opposed to language and literature subjects (ibid:33-34). There were six scales used in the SIMS study and none of these were comparative. Rather, they assessed students' attitudes towards mathematics per se.: mathematics as fun, mathematics as process, utility of mathematics, parents' attitudes, the self and mathematics and stereotyping in mathematics.

While there is some evidence from a small study (N=232) by Sugrue (1985:4) at primary level that girls in 5th class (age 11) have more positive attitudes towards mathematics than boys, there is no major study at primary level either confirming or contradicting this. What has been confirmed at both first and second level, however, is that boys rate themselves more highly than girls on their mathematical ability as well as on a range of other curricular areas (Kellaghan and Fontes, 1988:42-52; Hannan et al.,1983:34-36; Carey, 1990:231). There is also some evidence, although this does not accord with certain international indications, that better performance is related to better self image (Carey,1990).

The data on take-up rates suggest therefore, that while almost all girls and boys in Irish schools study mathematics up to the end of second level, more boys than girls tend to take the higher courses in the Senior Cycle (after age 15 approx.). While differences in take-up rates in the senior cycle higher courses are considerable, they have declined considerably in recent years:

In 1975 more than four times as many boys as girls did higher course mathematics for the Leaving Certificate (17.6% as opposed to 3.6%) and by 1983 the proportion of boys taking the higher courses was still almost three times that of girls (17.2% compared with 5.9%) (Carey, 1990:262). The current situation where 26% of boys as opposed to 15% of girls take the higher courses represents a considerable improvement on this. However, the available research still suggests that girls do not have the same confidence as boys in their mathematical abilities.

Performance

General Findings

While there is considerable evidence to suggest that Irish girls do not perform as well as boys in mathematics, this does not hold true either at all times, for all age groups, or in all studies. Girls' performance in some mathematics examinations is, in fact, superior to that of boys.

Research on a nationally representative sample of second class (age 8 approx.) and fourth class (age 10 approx.) pupils in 1977, and of sixth class (age 12 approx.) in both 1979 and 1984 (Department of Education, 1980;1985) showed that, while girls generally achieved higher levels of performance in mathematics in both second and fourth class, boys tended to do better in most objectives in sixth class (Greaney and Close,1989:54-55). Two studies of performance in mathematics and science have been conducted in Ireland in recent years by the US based Educational Testing Service in conjunction with the Educational Research Centre in Dublin (IAEP, 1989,1992). These studies have a number of limitations arising from their attempts, in certain respects, to compare the incomparable, in terms of both culture and curriculum practice (Oldham, 1991). Bearing these limitations in mind, we find what appears to be conflicting evidence regarding girls' performance in mathematics. In the 1989 study, no significant overall difference was found between thirteen year old Irish girls and boys in mathematics. The 1992 study found that there was an overall significant gender difference in mathematics performance in favour of boys. The decline in the performance of girls vis-a-vis boys between 1989 and 1992 is, however, most likely related to the fact that, in the latter survey there were substantially fewer (about 15% less) items on number and operations (items on which girls tend to do well) and correspondingly more on geometry (where girls tend to perform less well) and on algebra (where girls' performance is uneven) than in the earlier study. The 1992 study obtained data on nine year olds but this was not collected in the 1988 study; in this case girls and boys performed equally well in mathematics.

125

Another important source of data on mathematics performance in Ireland is the follow-up research to the SIMS study mentioned above. The material for this study was collected by Trinity College School of Education in 1985/86 with Maurice O'Driscoll, as National Research Co-ordinator. It has subsequently been used by Carey (1990) for her M.Ed. thesis in Trinity College. The study, which is based on a sample of 1651 first year students in second-level schools (approximately 45% of whom are thirteen years old: Oldham, 1991:125) found that boys did significantly better than girls both in the overall mathematics test and in the different content areas (Carey, 1990:154-162). Boys also performed significantly better than girls in each of the four mathematical cognitive categories, namely, computation, comprehension, application and analysis (ibid:162-166).

What is interesting to note from this study too is that both girls and boys in the 'higher' socio-economic groups performed better in all fields of mathematics than girls and boys in the 'lower' socio-economic groups. In addition, gender differences were found to be greater in the 'higher' than in the 'lower' groups.

The principal ongoing sources of data on mathematics performance in Ireland are the Intermediate (now Junior) Certificate and the Leaving Certificate Examinations; the former takes place after three years of second-level education while the latter is at the end of second level. Reviewing the results of these examinations, Carey (1990:44-54) found that a higher percentage of boys than girls not only passed the mathematics examination but passed with honours (Grade C or higher) each year from 1975- 1983 (see Appendix, Tables A9 and A10). She also found, however, that the gender gap in performance had narrowed over the years. Unfortunately, owing to an industrial relations dispute and funding problems, examination results for Irish public examinations were not published from 1983 to 1989 so we cannot comment on the trend over that period. Data from the 1990 examinations is presented below.

The results of the Intermediate and Leaving Certificate examinations in 1990 vary somewhat from those of Carey (1990) and the IAEP (1989,1992); they indicate that while the gender gap in mathematics is still notable, it may be diminishing. As Table V below shows, slightly more boys than girls obtained a grade C or higher in all three papers in the Intermediate Certificate Examinations; however, the differences here are very small and are not at all of the same magnitude as they were in 1983 (Appendix, Table A9).

Table V: Gender Differences in Mathematics in the Intermediate Certificate Examination 1990: Percentage of Students obtaining Grade C or higher

Subject	Girls		Boys	
	N	%	N	%
Mathematics A (higher)	5,909	67.8	6,545	69.7
Mathematics B (ordinary)	9,919	64.5	9,070	64.6
Mathematics C (lower)	2,450	44.9	2,481	49.3
Source Department of Education (1991) *Statistical Report 1989/90*: Tables 23a and 23b.				

For a detailed breakdown of grades in all subjects in the Intermediate for 1990 see Appendix Tables A5 and A6.

Unlike years 1975-1983, more boys than girls failed (i.e. obtained Grade E or less) on each of the three mathematics courses at Intermediate level (Table VI).

Table VI: The Proportion of Girls and Boys obtaining a Grade E or lower (a Fail) in Public Examinations in Mathematics in 1990

Examination	Girls	Boys
	%	%
Intermediate		
Mathematics A (higher)	5.9	6.0
Mathematics B (ordinary)	6.4	7.4
Mathematics C (lower)	17.5	17.7
Leaving Certificate		
Mathematics (H)	4.7	7.1
Mathematics (O)	18.6	18.3
Source:Department of Education (1991) Tables 23 (a) and (b) and Tables 24 (a) (b) (d) and (e)		

At Leaving Certificate level, we find that a slightly higher proportion of girls than boys obtain a grade C or higher in the higher level mathematics paper though the reverse is true in the ordinary level paper (Table VII). With regard to failure rates, there is no real difference between girls and boys in the ordinary mathematics paper; in the higher paper however, a noticeably higher proportion of boys (7.1%) compared with girls (4.7%) fail (Table VI). Once again, this is different to the pattern which obtained from 1975-1983.

Table VII: Gender Differences in a selected range of Subjects in the Leaving Certificate Examination, 1990:Percentage of Students obtaining Grade C or higher

Subject	Girls		Boys	
	N	%	N	%
Mathematics (H)*	1,674	69.2	2,999	69.0
Mathematics (O)	15,883	62.7	13,217	63.4
Physics (H)	1,290	67.6	3,305	66.3
Physics (O)	353	64.1	1,645	53.7
Chemistry (H)	1,768	58.7	2,302	66.6
Chemistry (O)	460	57.9	681	47.3
Biology (H)	6,849	65.1	3,136	64.1
Biology (O)	3,789	51.0	2,140	50.5
Irish (H)	5,440	76.2	2,727	63.9
Irish (O)	9,828	52.8	5,489	32.7
English (H)	8,773	62.7	5,983	54.2
English (O)	7,777	57.7	5,808	43.7
French (H)	6,259	65.4	3,549	56.5
French (O)	5,945	50.5	3,287	47.2
History (H)	2,048	61.7	2,099	55.5
History (O)	1,459	51.7	2,164	59.5
Accounting (H)	2,837	64.5	3,163	63.9
Acounting (O)	2,602	65.6	1,434	56.5

* (H) refers to the higher level papers and (O) to the ordinary level papers.

Source: Department of Education (1991) *Statistical Report 1989/90* Tables 24a, 24b, 24d, 24e. (For a more detailed breakdown of results in all subjects see Appendix Tables A5-A8).

What is interesting to note from Table VII above is that the differences between the sexes in mathematics and the sciences are generally very small, especially when compared with differences (in favour of girls) in languages, for example. It would seem therefore that while there is evidence that boys perform better than girls in mathematics, this does not hold true in all cases. Gender differences in performance seem to vary with the age of pupils, the level at which the subject is assessed, and whether an assessment is entirely curriculum-based (as the Leaving and Intermediate Certificate are) or not (as is true of the IAEP studies). There is also some evidence that the gender gap in mathematics, in which boys have persistently had an advantage, may be diminishing.

Performance by content Area and Cognitive Category

General test scores or examination grades in mathematics often mask substantial variations in sub-scores representing differential performance on specific content areas (e.g. numbers, geometry, measure) or categories of tasks relating to cognitive complexity (e.g concepts, procedures, problem-solving). Consequently, the presence of gender differences in total scores may be attributable more to one content area than another or to one category of task rather than another. There is a substantial body of research evidence which has identified significant gender related differences in sub-scores on mathematics tests, particularly in the upper grades of primary school and in secondary school.

Fennema (1974) reviewed 36 studies, mainly of children aged 10 to 15 years, and concluded that girls performed better than boys on tasks of low cognitive complexity (computation) while boys performed better than girls on tasks of high complexity (conceptual knowledge, applications and analysis). Similar results were obtained in the 1978, National Assessment of Education Progress in the US. (Fennema 1981). This study also revealed that gender differences, in favour of boys, were particularly large on items relating to geometry and measurement.

In Britain, the 1982 Assessment of Performance Unit Study (APU Survey) found small but significant differences in favour of boys in five content areas, differences which broadened considerably at the 15-plus level (Shuard, 1986). Girls performed better than boys on computation and algebra whereas boys performed better on measurement, applications, ratio and proportion.

Taking a cross-cultural perspective, the 1964 International Study of Achievement in Mathematics revealed that, at age 13, performance of boys was higher than that of girls in all 12 countries involved in the study (Husen, 1967). Boys lead in performance was greater in problem solving than in computation.

More recently Ethington (1990) analysed data for 13 year-olds in 8 countries who participated in the Second International Mathematics Study, carried out in 1981-82. Using an exploratory data analysis technique, she found no substantial gender effects in any of the content areas tested. Countries tested included United States, Japan, Belgium, France, New Zealand, Thailand, Ontario and British Columbia. However in analysing the SIMS data for 18 year-olds in fifteen countries, Hanna, Kündiger and Larouche (1990) found the mathematics achievement means for girls to be significantly lower than the means for boys. In five of the countries significant differences in favour of boys were found in six of the seven content areas tested.

Hanna (1986) used SIMS data on 3500 grade 8 students in Ontario schools to look at sex differences in the five content areas tested (arithmetic, algebra, geometry, statistics and measurement) She found no significant differences in arithmetic, algebra and statistics, but found statistically significant differences (about 3%) in geometry and measurement. These results indicate that gender differences are related to the type of mathematical task administered.

Ireland

A 1974 study of the mathematical attainments of Irish pupils in their first year of second level schooling (Kellaghan, Madaus, Airasian and Fontes, 1976) used a test of 55 objectives of the primary school mathematics programme. Most of the pupils in the sample were 13 years of age. Results (Table VIII below) showed that boys did significantly better than girls in seven out of the nine content areas tested. Girls did better than boys on operations with whole numbers and about the same as boys on whole number concepts.

The inspectorate of the Irish Department of Education administered tests of curriculum objectives in mathematics to nationally representative samples of pupils in 2nd class (8 year-olds) and 4th class (10 year-olds) in 1977, and in 6th class (12 year-olds) in 1979 (Department of Education,

Table VIII: Proportion of Girls and Boys Attaining Sets of Objectives:1st Year at Second-Level

Sets of Objectives	Boys	Girls
	%	%
A. Operations with Whole Numbers	67.63	72.17
B. Whole Number Structure	55.38	55.46
C. Fractional Number Structure	62.86	54.52
D. Operations with Fractions	50.87	45.18
E. Decimals and Percentages	56.46	43.98
F. Algebra	62.33	39.40
G. Geometry	66.17	46.50
H. Charts and Graphs	74.19	62.30
J. Arithmetical Problems	42.68	24.90

Source: Kellaghan et al.(1976)

TABLE IX: Results of Department of Education Survey: 1977 and 1979. Mean percentage of pupils meeting objectives by content area

	2nd Class		4th Class		6th Class	
	Boys	Girls	Boys	Girls	Boys	Girls
	%	%	%	%	%	%
Whole number computation	83	88	73	79	87	85
Whole number concepts	61	68	58	61	51	50
Fraction concepts	52	66	60	57	59	58
Fraction computation	-	-	-	-	70	70
Decimals	-	-	-	-	66	60
Measurement	55	58	60	57	53	36
Geometry	58	65	48	53	36	32
Charts and Graphs	51	60	50	56	57	62
Word Problems	58	63	41	41	58	46
Algebra	-	-	-	-	60	52

Source: Department of Education (1980)

1980). The mean percentages of boys and girls meeting objectives in ten content areas of the mathematics curriculum are given in Table IX above.

In 2nd class, girls significantly out-performed boys on all seven content areas tested. By 4th class, this advantage was reduced substantially and confined to four content areas; whole number computation, whole number concepts, geometry, and charts and graphs. Boys scored slightly better in measurement and fraction concepts. In 6th class, boys significantly out-performed girls in six content areas, including decimals, measurement, geometry, word problems and algebra. Performance on whole number computation and concepts, and fraction computation was similar for boys and girls, while girls scored higher than boys on charts and graphs.

Five years later, in 1984, a nationally representative sample of pupils in 6th class was administered a test which paralleled the test used in 1979. (Martin, 1990). The results are presented in Table X along with the 1979 6th class results.

Over the five years between 1979 and 1984, boys improved their performance in two areas: fractions and geometry but performance deteriorated in six areas: whole number computation and concepts, fraction computation, decimals, word problems, and algebra. Girls, on the other

Table X: Results of Department of Education Surveys 1979 and 1984 (6th Class, age 12): Mean percentage of pupils mastering objectives by content area.

	1979 %		1984 %	
	Boys	Girls	Boys	Girls
Whole number computation	87	85	82	85
Whole number concepts	51	50	49	54
Fraction cencepts	59	58	65	65
Fraction computation	70	70	67	75
Decimals	66	60	64	61
Measurement	53	36	53	44
Geometry	36	32	39	35
Charts and Graphs	57	62	58	60
Word Problems	58	46	53	49
Algebra	60	52	53	49
Source: Martin (1990)				

hand, improved their performance in six areas: whole number concepts, fraction concepts and computation, measurement, geometry, and word problems, but performance deteriorated in: charts and graphs and algebra. In 1984 girls outperformed boys in four areas: whole number computation and concepts, fraction computation, and charts and graphs, while boys did better than girls in five areas: decimals, measurement, geometry, word problems and algebra.

These results suggest that gender differences in mathematics had reduced significantly between 1979 and 1984, a reduction which can probably be ascribed to both educational and social factors such as changes in the teacher education programme for women, and rising expectations and opportunities for both boys and girls in the mathematical and science-related areas (Lynch,1992). It is interesting to note that the first cohort of male and female primary teachers to be trained together emerged from the Colleges of Education in 1974; prior to this only the Church of Ireland College of Education was co-educational, and this was very small compared with the other Roman-Catholic-controlled Colleges. The fact that most male and female teacher trainees were educated in separate colleges may well have had an adverse affect on mathematics education especially among women; historical evidence suggests that different standards of mathematics were required of male and female teachers, an example of this being that, prior to 1971, women teachers at primary level were not required to teach algebra and geometry (McGuinness and Oldham, 1982).

Data from two international studies (IAEP I and II) in which Ireland participated, provide more up to date information on gender differences in the mathematical performance of Irish 13 year olds. (Lapointe, Mead and Phillips, 1989; Lapointe, Mead and Askew, 1992). Tables XI (page 134) and XII (page 135) present the mathematical performances of boys and girls in these two studies broken down by content area and cognitive category. In the case of the 1988 study, boys did slightly better than girls overall (64.2% of boys mastered objectives compared with 61.9% of girls), but not significantly so. However it can be seen from Table XI that substantial differences exist in the areas of geometry and measurement (nearly 7% in favour of boys) and applications (5% in favour of boys.)

In the 1991 study overall differences between boys and girls were small but significant (62.6% for boys and 58.4% for girls) but here again

Table XI: IAEP (I) (1988): Mathematical performance of Irish 13 year-olds by gender, content area and cognitive category: Mean percentage with correct answers

Content Area			Cognitive Category		
	Boys	Girls		Boys	Girls
	%	%		%	%
Number	67.8	68.1	Factual Knowledge	67.4	65.2
Geometry	59.5	52.7	Skill	66.6	67.6
Measurement	58.3	51.8			
Data handling	49.9	46.0	Conceptual Knowledge	56.3	52.3
Algebra	68.9	69.0	Applications	65.7	60.7
Logic	72.6	71.0	Problem-solving	69.4	67.6

substantial differences emerged in geometry and measurement (about 7% in favour of boys) in algebra (about 4% in favour of boys) and in problem-solving (about 6% in favour of boys). It should be noted that the 1991 test differed from the 1988 test in that the 1991 test had substantially fewer items on areas where girls tend to do better (number and operations; about 15% less) and correspondingly more on geometry and algebra where boys tend to do better. Boys' scores tended to be spread out more than girls' scores, with more boys than girls in the top and bottom 10%, a pattern which is consistent with findings from earlier studies.

In the follow-up study to SIMS (with a more limited sample of Grade 8 pupils/1st year second level) Carey (1990) used the SIMS test and found substantial gender differences in favour of boys in algebra, measurement and geometry, but also found that these differences were strongly related to the social background of the pupils. Differences between boys and girls from farming backgrounds were negligible for all content areas apart from measurement, whereas differences were very substantial (and greatest) for all content areas in the case of boys and girls from the skilled workers category (Table XIII, p.135). To explain the significance of these social-class-related findings, much more research needs to be done. What they do indicate, however, is that there is a danger in treating boys and girls as homogeneous groups in the analysis of mathematical differences. There are very likely to be social class factors (and indeed racial, ethnic and disability factors) compounding gender differentials, so that gender differences are not identical across social groups.

Table XII: IAEP (II) (1991): Mathematical performance of Irish 13 year-olds by gender, content area and cognitive category: Mean percentage with correct answer

Content Area	Boys	Girls	Cognitive Category	Boys	Girls
	%	%		%	%
Number	66.2	64.1			
Geometry	63.2	56.6			
Measurement	53.3	45.4	Procedural knowledge	63.9	60.1
Data handling	72.8	70.8	Conceptual Understanding	63.2	59.8
Algebra	57.7	53.4	Problem-solving	60.7	55.1

In the case of IAEP (II) a representative sample of Irish 9 year olds was also surveyed. At this level there were no gender differences in the overall scores of boy and girls nor were there any within any content area or cognitive category with the exception of data handling/statistics where girls outperformed boys by 3%.

Table XIII: Gender Differences in Sub-test Scores by Socio-economic Status (Boys' Percentage Mean Minus Girls' Percentage Mean)

Subtest	Socioeconomic Categorisations				
	Unskilled	Skilled	Sales/Clerical	Professional	Farmer
Arithmetic	6.1	6.1	3.6	4.5	1.1
Algebra	2.3	8.9	5.5	5.8	2.0
Geometry	3.8	12.4	7.5	7.5	0.6
Statistics	4.5	3.7	1.8	3.3	-1.7
Measurement	9.5	12.8	8.4	9.1	9.2
Source: Carey 1990					

The above reviews seem to suggest that early in primary school girls tend to out-perform boys in mathematics generally but by the end of primary school and in the early years of secondary school this trend has been partly reversed, with boys doing better than girls in the content areas of geometry, measurement and algebra and in the cognitive category of prob-

135

lem-solving and applications. However the extent of these differences appears to have been reduced over the past 10 to 15 years. This pattern in the performance of Irish boys and girls over time and over type of mathematical tasks is somewhat similar to that which is apparent in many countries but also different from that of other countries, strongly suggesting that differences are culturally and educationally determined.

Styles of Assessment and Gender Difference

As already mentioned, Irish students sit for their first public examination (the Junior Certificate, formerly the Intermediate Certificate) at the end of their period of compulsory schooling (age 15) and for their second (the Leaving Certificate) at the end of second level. These are summative examinations conducted in a conventional examination format.

In 1989 a new programme was put in place (the Junior Certificate) for the first 3 years of second-level education; it was examined for the first time in 1992. Efforts have been made to include more oral, aural, practical and project work in the new Junior Certificate Examination. The current *Green Paper (1992)* indicates that this is now official government policy, at least for the Junior Cycle of second-level schools. However, the efforts are not likely to be entirely successful in the short term as there are insufficient resources available to provide the necessary inservice education and compensation for teachers for the extra work involved. In addition, there is considerable concern about the principle of continuous assessment and teacher/school-based assessment among teachers especially. A recently published discussion paper commissioned by one of the major teacher unions outlines a number of these concerns (Williams, 1992). It is pointed out that systems of continuous and school-based assessment are highly labour intensive and both require external monitoring. There is a fear that the kind of resources required to run this type of system effectively (as happens in Germany, for example) are simply not available in Ireland. In addition, there is no historical precedent for an examiner-examinee-type of pedagogical relationship between teachers and pupils in second-level education in Ireland. The tradition has been the very opposite; teachers and students tend to form an alliance 'against' the public examination system. There is a genuine fear on the part of teachers that, if they were to become the assessors of their students, the character of teaching would change radically. Also, there is the problem of parental pressure being exerted on teachers, particularly in a small-scale society like Ireland where parents and teachers can be known to each other on a personal basis especially in small towns and rural areas. While teachers do not deny that there are serious weaknesses with the present summative form which public examinations take (ibid:46-59) there is fear that an alternative continuous and/or school-based system may be even less fair and effective because of lack of finance. Because of these dilemmas, it is unlikely, therefore, that there will be any change in the way courses are taught or assessed in the Junior (or, to an even greater degree, in the Leaving) Certificate Examination in mathematics in the near future. In addition, because selection for higher education institutions is now based entirely on Leaving Certificate grades, the possibility for greater flexibility in modes of assessment has lessened if anything at the senior level.

Mathematics

Like most other subjects, mathematics is assessed at both junior and senior level by summative unseen public examinations. Up to 1976, the Intermediate Certificate Examination in mathematics was entirely made up of free response (or essay type) questions. From 1976 onwards the mathematics examination included a multiple-choice section on each of the two papers for which up to one third of the total marks available could be obtained. The multiple-choice section was dropped from 1990 onwards following pressure from mathematics teachers who felt that the students got no credit for partial solutions using the multiple-choice format.

In a recently published study, Bolger and Kellaghan (1990) examined 1,500 male and female students who were in their third year of secondary school, in terms of their performance on standardised multiple-choice tests of mathematics, Irish and English compared with their performance on the essay-type questions on the Intermediate Certificate Examinations in these subjects. In all three subjects, boys performed significantly better on multiple-choice tests than on free-response tests; conversely, girls did better in free-response examinations. The standardised tests were administered in the middle of the school year and the students sat the Intermediate Certificate Examination at the end of the School year. Table XIV (see page 138) presents the results (with raw scores converted to z scores) for mathematics.

Table XIV: Means and standard deviations for multiple-choice and free response measures of achievement in mathematics by gender (in z scores, ie standard deviation units)			
	Multiple Choice		Free Response
	Mean	.269	.163
Males	(S.D.)	(.992)	(1.004)
	Mean	-.262	-.159
Females	(S.D)	.936	(.970)
Gender Difference (Female-male)		-.531	-.322
Source: Bolger and Kellaghan (1990)			

The results show that males score one-third of a standard deviation higher than females on the free-response test and about one half of a standard deviation higher on the multiple-choice test. Gender differences in the language areas were much less pronounced and favoured the girls. The authors speculated on reasons for the differences, including (i) the possibility that males have a greater tendency to guess than females, (ii) that the examiners of the Intermediate Certificate Examination knew the gender of their examinees and that (iii) girls responded less well to the unfamiliar standardised tests than did the boys.

Conclusion

Mathematics is a subject which is studied by almost all (99%) girls and boys in Irish second level schools. Boys are still more likely, however, to study the higher courses in mathematics at the senior level although the gender gap is closing here. Indeed, in 1989/1990 there was a slightly higher proportion of girls than boys studying higher mathematics at the junior level: 44% compared with 42% (Table IV above).

One of the areas in which boys and girls differ significantly in relation to mathematics, is in terms of confidence in their mathematical ability: boys have been found to rate themselves more highly in the mathematics field at both primary and second level. Boys are also generally more likely to perform better in mathematics examinations; however, this does not hold true for all ages, for all content areas within the subject, or in all types of assessments. There is considerable evidence that the gender gap in performance has diminished considerably in recent years especially in curriculum-based public examinations. This concurs with findings elsewhere (Feingold, 1988).

The styles of assessment used in mathematics have not changed in Ireland in recent years. Oldham (1992:134) points out that Junior Cycle mathematics at second level is traditional in both content and style. A revised Junior syllabus was introduced in 1987 with three courses (A, B, C) being introduced in descending order of abstraction. She suggests that the outcome of the curriculum review was 'a battery of three courses shorn of some of the abstractions of earlier years, but perhaps not specifically designed to meet needs or opportunities in the late eighties and nineties and still presented in the style of earlier years' (ibid. 142).

In the revision of curricula, there appears to have been no serious discussion of gender issues. Given that girls are often the so-called weaker students in mathematics and that one of the Junior Cycle Committee's main tasks was 'to provide appropriately for weaker students' (ibid:141) this appears strange. It appears as if there was no connection made between the competence of students and their gender especially in those areas of mathematics where girls were doing badly. In the review of senior cycle mathematics that is currently under way, there is little evidence either that gender issues are central to the debate, either in terms of curriculum or in terms of modes of assessment (Oldham, 1993).

While there has been a debate in Ireland about assessment, the agenda for the debate has been set on issues of payment rather than gender. The crux of the matter is that teachers have not agreed to take part in any new continuous assessment procedures without in-service training and increased payment. The Department of Education has been unwilling to concede these claims for financial reasons, hence the deadlock in the debate. Even when the issue of assessment is raised outside of this context, as yet there does not appear to have been any serious consideration given to gender issues, in terms of the appropriateness of different modes of assessment for girls.

References

Bolger, N., and Kellaghan, T. (1990) Method of measurement and gender differences in scholastic achievement *Journal of Educational Measurement,* 27: 165-174

Carey,M., (1990) 'Gender Differences in Attitudes and Achievement in Mathematics — A Study of First Year Students in Irish Post-Primary Schools' Unpublished M.Ed. Thesis, School of Education, Trinity College.

Clancy, P.,(1987). 'Does School Type Matter? The Unresolved Questions', *Sociological Association of Ireland Bulletin,* No. 49, April, pp. 12-14.

Clancy, P., (1988). *Who Goes to College? A Second National Survey of Participation in Higher Education,* Dublin: The Higher Education Authority.

Clancy, P.,(1989). 'Gender Differences in Student Participation at Third Level' in C. Hussey (ed.), *Equal Opportunities for Women in Higher Education,* Dublin: University College Dublin

Council of Europe (1982). *Sex Stereotyping in Schools,* Lisse: Swets and Zeitlinger.

Department of Education, (1971). Primary School Curriculum : Teacher's Handbook, Dublin: Government Publications Office.

Department of Education (1974) *Statistical Report 1972/73.* Dublin: Government Publications Office.

Department of Education (1980) *Tuairisc ar Theagasc na Matamaitice sna* (An dara heagran) Dublin: Government Publications Office.

Department of Education (1985) *Tuairisc ar an Mhatamaitic in Rang VI.* Dublin Government Publications Office.

Department of Education (1991) *Statistical Report 1989/90.* Dublin: Government Publications Office.

Department of Education (1992) *Green Paper on Education: Education for a Changing World* Dublin: Government Publications Office.

Ethington, C. A. (1990) Gender differences in mathematics: An international perspective. *Journal for Research in Mathematics Education,* 21: 74-80

Feingold, A., (1988) 'Cognitive Gender Differences Are Disappearing', *American Psychologist,* 43:95-103.

Fennema, E. (1974) Mathematics learning and the sexes:A review. *Journal for Research in Mathematics Education.* 5: 126-139.

Fennema, E, and Carpenter, T.P. (1981) Sex related differences in mathematics: Results from National Assessment. *Mathematics Teacher,* 74, 554-559.

Greaney, V., and Kellaghan, T., (1984). *Equality of Opportunity in Irish Schools,* Dublin: The Educational Company.

Greaney,V., and Close, S., (1989) 'Mathematics Achievement in Irish Primary Schools', *The Irish Journal of Education*, Vol.xxii, No.2 : 51-64

Hanna, G. (1986) Sex differences in mathematics achievement of eight graders in Ontario. *Journal for Research in Mathematics Education:* 17, 231-237

Hanna, G., Kündiger, E. and Larouche, C., (1990) 'Mathematical Achievement of grade 12 girls in Fifteen Countries' in L. Burton (ed.) *Gender and Mathematics: An International Perspective*, London: Cassell.

Hannan, D., et al., (1983). *Schooling and Sex Roles*, Dublin: Economic and Social Research Institute, Paper No. 113.

Higher Education Authority (1975/76 and 1984/85). *Accounts and Student Statistics*, Dublin: Higher Education Authority.

Higher Education Authority (1991). *First Destination of Award Recipients in Higher Education.* Dublin: Higher Education Authority.

Husen, T. (1967) *International Study of Achievement in mathematics: a comparison of twelve countries.* Almquist and Wicksell and John Wiley. London.

International Association of Educational Progress (IAEP) (1989) *A World of Differences: An International Assessment of Mathematics and Science,* New Jersey: Educational Testing Service.

International Association of Educational Progress (IAEP) (1992) *Learning Mathematics.* New Jersey: Educational Testing Service.

International Association of Educational Progress (IAEP) (1992) *Learning Science.* New Jersey: Educational Testing Service.

Kellaghan, T., Madaus, G., Airasian, P., and Fontes, P. (1976) The mathematical attainments of post-primary entrants. *Irish Journal of Education* 10: 3-22.

Kellaghan, T.,Fontes, P.,et al., (1985). Gender Inequalities in Primary School Teaching, Dublin: The Educational Company.

Kellaghan,T., and Fontes, P.J., (1988) 'Gender Differences in the Scholastic Self-concepts of Irish Pupils', *Irish Journal of Education,* Vol.22:42-52.

Lapointe, A.E., Mead, N.A., and Phillips, G.W. (1989) (IAEP, 1989 is the same study) *A world of differences: an international assessment of mathematics and science.* Princeton, N.J. Education Testing Service.

Lapointe, A.E., Mead, N. A., and Askew, J.M. (1992) *Learning Mathematics.* Princeton, N.J. Education Testing Service.

Lynch, K., (1989). *The Hidden Curriculum: Reproduction in Education, A Reappraisal* London: Falmer Press.

Lynch, K., (1991) 'Girls and young Women in Education:Ireland' in M. Wilson (ed) *Girls and Young women in Education: A European Perspective.* Oxford: Pergamon.

Lynch, K., (1992) 'Education and the Paid Labour Market', *Irish Educational Studies*, Vol. 11: 13-33

McGuinness, P.J. and E.F. Oldham (1982) 'Gender and Mathematics in Ireland' in E. Schildkamp-Kundiger (ed.) *An International Review of Gender and Mathematics*, Columbia, Ohio: ERIC Clearinghouse, Ohio State University

Marland, M. (ed.) (1983). *Sex Differentiation and Schooling,* London: Heinemann.

Martin, M.O. (1990) Mathematics achievement in sixth class in Irish primary schools. *Irish Journal of Education* 22 (In press)

NCCA (National Council for Curriculum and Assessment) *The 1991 Leaving Certificate Examination: A Review of Results.* Dublin: NCCA.

Oldham, E., (1991) 'Second Level Mathematics Curricula: The Republic of Ireland in International Perspective', *Irish Educational Studies,* Vol. 10, No. 1, Spring:122-138.

Oldham, E., (1992) 'Junior Cycle Mathematics Curricula in the Republic of Ireland 1960-1990: Genesis, Exodus and Numbers', *Irish Educational Studies*, Vol.11: 134-150.

Oldham, E., (1993) 'Leaving Certificate Mathematics Curricula in the Republic of Ireland: courses for the 1990s'. *Irish Educational Studies*, Vol.12: 73-91.

Oldham, E., and P.J. McGuinness (1981) 'Gender and Mathematics: Ireland', Unpublished Paper, School of Education, Trinity College Dublin.

Sugrue, B., (1985) 'Gender Differences in Mathematics Achievement and Attitudes Among Fifth Class Pupils in Dublin in Primary Schools', *Studies in Education,* Vol.3., No.2:7-20.

Shuard, H. (1986) *Primary Mathematics Today and Tomorrow.* Longman for School Curriculum Development Committee. York.

Stanworth, Michelle (1983). *Gender and Schooling,* London: Hutchinson and Co.

Tansey, J., (1978) Selected Perspectives on Girls' Secondary School Education in the Republic of Ireland, 1925-1975. (Unpublished M.Ed. thesis, School of Education, Trinity College Dublin).

Williams, K., (1992) *Assessment: A Discussion Paper.* Dublin: Association of Secondary Teachers

Wilson, M. (ed.) (1991) *Girls and Young Women in Education: A European Perspective*, Oxford: Pergamon

WITS (Women in Technology and Science) (1991) Submission to the Second Commission on the Status of Women. Dublin.

The authors would like to thank the following people for their help in preparing this paper: Dr. Thomas Kellaghan, Director of the Educational Research Centre, St. Patrick's College, Drumcondra for his helpful comments; Ms. Margaret Carey for making data from her M.Ed. thesis at Trinity College available to us, and the Statistics branch of the Department of Education (Mr. Paul Gully especially) for providing us with a breakdown of statistics on the major public examinations.

APPENDIX TABLE A1

PERCENTAGE OF SCHOOLS PROVIDING THE STATED SUBJECT
BY CATEGORY OF SCHOOL

INTERMEDIATE CERTIFICATE
TOTAL POST PRIMARY

Subject / Category of School	Total	Single Sex Schools		Mixed Schools	Within Mixed Schools		
		Boys	Girls		To Boys Only	To Girls Only	To Both Sexes
1. Irish (H.C.)	81.6	87.3	91.8	74.3	1.2	0.2	72.9
2. Irish (L.C.)	84.5	87.3	89.2	81.1	1.5	—	79.7
3. Irish (C.C.)	17.7	8.8	12.8	24.0	—	—	24.0
4. English (H.C.)	82.8	89.5	91.8	75.5	1.2	—	74.3
5. English (L.C.)	81.1	81.8	84.1	79.4	1.5	—	78.0
6. English (C.C.)	17.9	9.4	11.8	24.5	—	—	24.5
7. Maths (H.C.)	82.9	88.4	91.3	76.5	2.2	—	74.3
8. Maths (L.C.)	85.9	89.0	89.7	82.8	1.2	—	81.6
9. Maths (C.C.)	18.8	9.4	14.4	24.9	—	—	24.9
10. History and/or Geography	94.8	95.6	96.4	93.7	1.0	0.7	92.0
11. Latin	7.6	17.1	10.3	2.2	0.2	—	1.9
12. Greek	0.5	1.7	0.5	—	—	—	—
13. Hebrew Studies	0.1	—	—	0.2	—	—	0.2
14. French	95.4	94.5	99.5	93.9	0.2	1.2	92.5
15. German	44.1	42.5	67.2	33.9	1.0	1.2	31.7
16. Spanish	10.1	10.5	18.5	6.1	0.5	—	5.6
17. Italian	0.8	1.7	1.0	0.2	0.2	—	—
18. Science A	85.8	92.8	92.3	79.7	0.7	0.5	78.5
19. Science E	17.5	3.3	1.5	31.2	1.7	0.2	29.3
20. Science (C.C.)	6.1	3.3	6.2	7.3	0.2	0.2	6.8
21. Home Economics	73.8	1.1	98.5	93.9	—	35.1	58.8
22. Music and Musicianship	45.4	29.3	77.4	37.3	0.2	6.8	30.3
23. Art	82.5	72.9	96.9	79.9	1.5	4.1	74.3
24. Woodwork	59.2	56.9	0.5	87.9	47.9	—	40.0
25. Metalwork	38.8	19.9	—	65.4	40.9	—	24.5
26. Mechanical Drawing	66.3	75.7	1.0	93.0	29.3	—	63.7
27. Commerce	91.9	91.2	88.7	93.7	0.5	15.3	78.0
28. Civics	80.4	92.3	93.8	68.8	1.0	0.2	67.6
29. Physical Education	83.0	84.5	95.9	76.3	—	0.7	75.5
30. Humanities	4.7	6.1	3.1	4.8	0.7	—	4.1
31. Environmental Studies	2.0	1.1	5.6	0.7	—	—	0.7
32. Classical Studies	3.4	7.2	3.6	1.7	—	—	1.7
33. Computer Studies	26.1	29.8	22.1	26.4	1.0	0.7	24.7

* Source of Tables A1 - A8: Department of Education (1991) <u>Statistical Report</u>. Dublin: Government Publications.

APPENDIX TABLE A2

PERCENTAGE OF SCHOOLS PROVIDING THE STATED SUBJECT
BY CATEGORY OF SCHOOL

LEAVING CERTIFICATE
TOTAL POST PRIMARY

Category of School / Subject	Total	Single Sex Schools		Mixed Schools	Within Mixed Schools		
		Boys	Girls		To Boys Only	To Girls Only	To Both Sexes
1. Irish (H.C.)	81.4	89.5	89.9	74.5	1.6	1.4	71.5
2. Irish (L.C.)	86.6	90.1	89.9	83.8	0.9	0.5	82.4
3. Irish (C.C.)	15.1	8.0	11.6	19.2	—	—	19.2
4. English (H.C.)	84.4	91.4	91.0	78.9	1.4	0.5	77.1
5. English (L.C.)	86.1	89.5	88.4	83.8	2.3	0.5	81.0
6. English (C.C.)	17.0	9.9	14.3	20.8	—	0.2	20.6
7. Latin	6.4	14.2	7.9	2.8	0.7	0.2	1.9
8. Greek	0.6	1.9	0.5	0.2	0.2	—	—
9. Hebrew Studies	0.1	—	—	0.2	—	—	0.2
10. French	95.7	95.7	99.5	94.0	0.9	3.5	89.6
11. German	30.3	22.2	55.0	22.5	0.7	2.1	19.7
12. Italian	1.1	1.2	2.1	0.7	0.5	—	0.2
13. Spanish	11.9	9.3	23.3	7.9	0.9	1.2	5.8
14. History	84.5	92.0	97.4	76.2	2.8	1.9	71.5
15. Geography	87.6	95.1	94.2	81.9	2.5	1.2	78.2
16. Maths (H.C.)	80.1	90.7	89.4	72.0	10.4	0.7	60.9
17. Maths (L.C.)	90.7	93.2	95.2	87.7	0.7	0.2	86.8
18. Maths (C.C.)	10.7	5.6	5.3	15.0	—	—	15.0
19. Applied Maths	13.9	32.1	5.3	10.9	2.5	—	8.3
20. Physics	75.5	92.6	78.8	67.6	7.9	0.2	59.5
21. Chemistry	67.0	87.0	88.9	50.0	1.9	0.7	47.5
22. Physics and Chemistry	15.1	12.3	6.3	19.9	2.3	0.2	17.4
23. Agricultural Science	17.1	21.0	2.6	22.0	5.6	0.2	16.2
24. Biology	93.6	87.7	97.9	94.0	1.4	3.7	88.9
25. Agricultural Economics ..	2.4	3.7	0.5	2.8	0.7	—	2.1
26. Engineering	35.6	13.0	0.5	59.5	42.1	—	17.4
27. Technical Drawing	60.3	62.3	3.2	84.5	47.0	—	37.5
28. Construction Studies	41.5	29.6	—	64.1	46.8	—	17.4
29. Home Economics (S.S.)	75.4	19.1	97.4	86.8	—	26.6	60.2
30. Home Economics (General) ..	16.3	1.9	33.3	14.4	—	7.9	6.5
31. Accounting	78.8	85.2	83.1	74.5	1.2	7.2	66.2
32. Business Organisation	81.2	85.8	85.7	77.5	0.9	6.5	70.1
33. Economics	44.1	68.5	41.8	35.9	1.4	—	34.5
34. Economic History	1.1	2.5	1.1	0.7	—	0.2	0.5
35. Art (Incl.Crafts)	78.0	64.8	95.8	75.2	2.1	4.4	68.8
36. Music and Musicianship	26.4	13.6	57.7	17.6	0.9	4.2	12.5
37. Physical Education	67.6	63.6	85.7	61.1	1.9	1.2	58.1
38. Classical Studies	2.3	4.9	3.2	0.9	—	—	0.9

Source: Department of Education (1991)

APPENDIX TABLE A3

PERCENTAGE OF BOYS AND GIRLS
TAKING THE STATED SUBJECT

INTERMEDIATE CERTIFICATE
TOTAL POST PRIMARY

Category of School / Subject	BOYS	GIRLS
1. Irish (H.C.)	38.2	45.2
2. Irish (L.C.)	49.4	41.8
3. Irish (C.C.)	11.0	12.0
4. English (H.C.)	46.4	55.2
5. English (L.C.)	39.3	31.2
6. English (C.C.)	11.2	11.6
7. Maths (H.C.)	42.1	44.4
8. Maths (L.C.)	46.5	43.1
9. Maths (C.C.)	11.1	12.4
10. History and/or Geography ..	88.5	92.3
11. Latin	3.0	1.5
12. Greek	0.1	—
13. Hebrew Studies	—	—
14. French	63.1	79.7
15. German	13.9	20.9
16. Spanish	2.2	3.1
17. Italian	0.1	—
18. Science A	78.1	68.0
19. Science E	11.2	5.6
20. Science (C.C.)	4.2	4.0
21. Home Economics	4.7	62.8
22. Music and Musicianship ..	8.8	24.2
23. Art	32.8	48.6
24. Woodwork	44.6	2.6
25. Metalwork	30.1	1.1
26. Mechanical Drawing	56.3	4.8
27. Commerce..	54.9	70.3
28. Civics	78.4	82.8
29. Physical Education	82.6	91.3
30. Humanities	3.1	2.4
31. Environmental Studies	0.5	2.2
32. Classical Studies..	1.3	0.8
33. Computer Studies	17.6	15.6

Source: Department of Education (1991)

APPENDIX TABLE A4

PERCENTAGE OF BOYS AND GIRLS
TAKING THE STATED SUBJECT

LEAVING CERTIFICATE
TOTAL POST PRIMARY

Category of School Subject	BOYS	GIRLS
1. Irish (H.C.)	28.4	34.0
2. Irish (L.C.)	60.2	54.7
3. Irish (C.C.)	7.3	8.7
4. English (H.C.)..	44.4	48.8
5. English (L.C.)	44.6	40.0
6. English (C.C.)	8.6	9.6
7. Latin	1.3	0.3
8. Greek	—	—
9. Hebrew Studies	—	—
10. French	51.0	73.0
11. German	4.4	9.5
12. Italian	0.1	0.1
13. Spanish	1.2	2.4
14. History	27.6	22.5
15. Geography	40.6	31.0
16. Maths (H.C.)	26.1	15.0
17. Maths (L.C.)	65.3	77.1
18. Maths (C.C.)	6.7	6.3
19. Applied Maths..	3.5	0.4
20. Physics	31.0	9.6
21. Chemistry	18.8	13.4
22. Physics and Chemistry	4.9	2.2
23. Agricultural Science	7.6	1.2
24. Biology	35.7	60.1
25. Agricultural Economics	0.7	0.1
26. Engineering	16.4	0.4
27. Technical Drawing	29.1	0.9
28. Construction Studies	19.1	0.4
29. Home Economics (S.S.)	5.8	49.9
30. Home Economics (General)..	0.5	5.9
31. Accounting..	26.3	28.3
32. Business Organisation	35.0	41.7
33. Economics	17.5	9.0
34. Economic History	0.1	—
35. Art (Including Crafts)	13.7	22.5
36. Music and Musicianship	1.2	3.8
37. Physical Education	58.5	72.7
38. Classical Studies	0.5	0.2

Source: Department of Education (1991)

APPENDIX TABLE A5

LEAVING CERTIFICATE RESULTS 1990
PERCENTAGE BREAKDOWN OF CANDIDATES
BY GRADE AWARDED IN EACH SUBJECT
ORDINARY LEVEL PAPERS - MALE

Subject	Total Number of Candidates	Grade A	Grade B	Grade C	Grade D	Grade E	Grade F	No Grade
1. Irish	16,774	0.5	6.8	25.4	37.4	15.3	11.7	2.9
2. English	13,295	0.4	6.5	36.8	48.1	7.4	0.8	—
3. Latin	32	—	21.9	21.9	37.5	9.4	6.3	3.1
4. Greek	0	—	—	—	—	—	—	—
5. French	6,965	0.2	8.4	38.6	40.9	10.3	1.6	—
6. German	368	0.3	12.2	44.3	35.3	6.0	1.6	0.3
7. Italian	12	—	—	8.3	66.7	16.7	8.3	—
8. Spanish	137	8.0	10.9	42.3	29.9	5.8	2.2	0.7
9. History	3,637	8.5	22.5	28.5	24.3	8.7	5.7	1.8
10. Geography	4,188	1.5	17.0	44.8	30.5	5.5	0.6	0.1
11. Mathematics	20,865	11.0	29.9	22.5	18.3	9.1	7.0	2.2
12. Applied Mathematics	191	28.3	19.9	15.2	19.4	5.2	8.9	3.1
13. Physics	3,069	4.1	22.1	27.5	23.4	14.0	8.3	0.7
14. Chemistry	1,438	3.8	15.6	27.9	28.4	13.9	9.0	1.3
15. Physics & Chemistry	561	3.6	17.5	29.4	27.5	14.1	7.1	0.9
16. Biology	4,241	1.8	17.1	31.6	27.5	13.7	7.0	1.3
17. Agricultural Science	785	—	3.2	24.1	50.1	17.3	5.4	—
18. Agricultural Economics	94	—	3.2	29.8	40.4	21.3	5.3	—
19. Home Economics (Scientific & Social)	916	0.9	10.5	31.6	42.0	11.4	3.3	0.4
20. Home Economics (General)	38	—	—	31.6	34.2	15.8	18.4	—
21. Accounting	2,540	3.8	23.4	29.3	23.8	10.2	6.0	3.6
22. Business Organisation	4,350	2.5	19.1	37.7	31.5	7.2	1.7	0.2
23. Economics	1,913	3.3	18.6	28.6	34.5	7.9	5.6	1.5
24. Economic History	21	—	4.8	19.0	52.4	19.0	4.8	—
25. Art	1,533	1.8	8.4	31.1	47.7	9.1	1.7	0.1
26. Music & Musicianship - A	39	—	—	7.7	56.4	33.3	2.6	—
27. Music & Musicianship - B	8	—	—	50.0	37.5	12.5	—	—
28. Engineering	1,710	0.3	13.2	50.3	32.9	2.9	0.5	—
29. Technical Drawing	4,328	5.5	22.9	28.2	28.3	11.2	3.5	0.4
30. Construction Studies	1,991	0.3	10.7	36.4	41.9	9.3	1.4	0.1
31. Hebrew	1	—	—	—	100.0	—	—	—
32. Classical Studies	19	—	10.5	15.8	42.1	15.8	15.8	—

*Data refer to School Candidates only

APPENDIX TABLE A6

LEAVING CERTIFICATE RESULTS 1990
PERCENTAGE BREAKDOWN OF CANDIDATES
BY GRADE AWARDED IN EACH SUBJECT
ORDINARY LEVEL PAPERS - FEMALE

	Subject	Total Number of Candidates	Grade A	Grade B	Grade C	Grade D	Grade E	Grade F	No Grade
1.	Irish	18,633	1.5	15.7	35.6	31.9	9.9	4.6	0.9
2.	English	13,458	0.6	9.7	47.4	38.4	3.5	0.3	—
3.	Latin	10	—	20.0	20.0	30.0	10.0	20.0	—
4.	Greek	0	—	—	—	—	—	—	—
5.	French	11,784	0.2	10.8	39.5	39.6	8.8	1.1	—
6.	German	628	1.3	24.2	43.8	26.0	4.0	0.8	—
7.	Italian	9	—	—	11.1	33.3	55.6	—	—
8.	Spanish	302	4.0	8.9	31.1	41.7	11.3	3.0	—
9.	History	2,822	7.0	19.5	25.2	27.4	10.1	8.2	2.7
10.	Geography	3,394	3.1	17.5	39.9	30.2	7.8	1.4	0.1
11.	Mathematics	25,340	9.6	29.0	24.1	18.8	9.4	7.1	2.1
12.	Applied Mathematics	31	32.3	35.5	19.4	9.7	3.2	—	—
13.	Physics	551	5.3	30.9	27.9	20.5	9.1	6.2	0.2
14.	Chemistry	795	5.8	21.4	30.7	26.4	10.1	5.3	0.4
15.	Physics & Chemistry	101	5.9	15.8	32.7	21.8	16.8	5.9	1.0
16.	Biology	7,427	2.0	18.4	30.6	28.2	13.5	6.3	0.9
17.	Agricultural Science	154	—	3.9	14.3	55.8	22.1	3.9	—
18.	Agricultural Economics	6	—	33.3	33.3	33.3	—	—	—
19.	Home Economics (Scientific & Social)	5,084	2.3	22.0	40.0	28.9	5.6	1.0	0.2
20.	Home Economics (General)	918	2.3	18.8	43.1	28.4	6.5	0.8	—
21.	Accounting	3,971	6.2	27.3	32.1	23.1	8.1	2.8	0.5
22.	Business Organisation	6,228	2.4	16.3	36.0	33.1	9.2	2.6	0.3
23.	Economics	1,115	3.8	16.0	25.7	33.7	8.1	10.8	2.0
24.	Economic History	3	—	—	—	33.3	33.3	33.3	—
25.	Art	2,560	2.3	10.1	36.7	43.5	6.6	0.8	—
26.	Music & Musicianship - A	189	—	1.1	17.5	59.3	19.0	2.6	0.5
27.	Music & Musicianship - B	24	—	8.3	29.2	41.7	20.8	—	—
28.	Engineering	52	—	5.8	32.7	51.9	9.6	—	—
29.	Technical Drawing	145	2.8	22.1	20.7	31.0	16.6	6.2	0.7
30.	Construction Studies	43	—	4.7	32.6	39.5	23.3	—	—
31.	Hebrew	0	—	—	—	—	—	—	—
32.	Classical Studies	16	—	25.0	50.0	18.8	6.3	—	—

*Data refer to School Candidates only

149

APPENDIX TABLE A7

LEAVING CERTIFICATE RESULTS 1990
PERCENTAGE BREAKDOWN OF CANDIDATES
BY GRADE AWARDED IN EACH SUBJECT
HIGHER LEVEL PAPERS - MALE

Subject	Total Number of Candidates	Grade A	Grade B	Grade C	Grade D	Grade E	Grade F	No Grade
1. Irish	4,266	3.3	19.1	41.5	31.8	2.7	0.5	1.1
2. English	11,030	2.9	14.1	37.2	39.9	5.5	0.3	—
3. Latin	367	10.6	30.0	31.6	21.3	5.7	0.5	0.3
4. Greek	13	15.4	46.2	23.1	15.4	—	—	—
5. French	6,284	2.4	16.0	38.1	36.4	6.6	0.4	—
6. German	554	5.8	19.7	36.5	31.6	6.3	0.2	—
7. Italian	28	7.1	21.4	25.0	39.3	3.6	3.6	—
8. Spanish	205	22.0	13.2	31.2	29.8	3.9	—	—
9. History	3,781	5.2	15.8	34.5	32.8	8.8	2.2	0.6
10. Geography	6,669	3.0	13.3	41.5	35.9	5.5	0.6	0.2
11. Mathematics	4,348	8.7	25.8	34.5	24.0	5.7	1.2	0.2
12. Applied Mathematics	906	19.1	23.7	27.7	20.5	6.7	2.1	0.1
13. Physics	4,986	6.6	31.9	27.8	24.9	6.4	2.3	0.1
14. Chemistry	3,462	9.0	27.1	30.5	21.8	9.2	2.4	0.1
15. Physics & Chemistry	699	3.7	20.9	30.2	29.6	12.9	2.3	0.4
16. Biology	4,897	3.5	23.1	37.5	24.9	9.3	1.6	0.2
17. Agricultural Science	1,054	1.9	18.8	45.0	28.3	5.3	0.8	—
18. Agricultural Economics	105	1.9	21.0	30.5	32.4	9.5	4.8	—
19. Home Economics (Scientific & Social)	1,210	1.2	10.5	27.4	39.3	17.0	3.6	1.0
20. Home Economics (General)	11	—	18.2	36.4	36.4	—	9.1	—
21. Accounting	4,950	4.6	28.5	30.8	22.5	9.7	3.5	0.4
22. Business Organisation	5,469	3.3	16.6	34.9	33.2	9.7	2.0	0.2
23. Economics	2,933	4.7	21.4	30.4	29.5	10.1	3.1	0.7
24. Economic History	53	37.7	39.6	20.8	1.9	—	—	—
25. Art	2,063	2.8	12.3	38.2	37.5	8.3	0.9	—
26. Music & Musicianship - A	36	2.8	8.3	19.4	55.6	11.1	2.8	—
27. Music & Musicianship - B	104	8.7	24.0	35.6	25.0	6.7	—	—
28. Engineering	1,859	5.1	39.0	44.7	10.7	0.5	—	—
29. Technical Drawing	2,458	5.0	21.6	32.8	27.7	10.2	2.6	0.1
30. Construction Studies	2,245	3.4	30.7	50.3	14.8	0.8	—	—
31. Hebrew	3	—	—	33.3	66.7	—	—	—
32. Classical Studies	135	3.0	20.7	26.7	36.3	8.1	4.4	0.7

*Data refer to School Candidates only

APPENDIX TABLE A8

LEAVING CERTIFICATE RESULTS 1990
PERCENTAGE BREAKDOWN OF CANDIDATES
BY GRADE AWARDED IN EACH SUBJECT
HIGHER LEVEL PAPERS - FEMALE

Subject	Total Number of Candidates	Grade A	Grade B	Grade C	Grade D	Grade E	Grade F	No Grade
1. Irish	7,145	5.4	26.4	44.4	22.4	1.2	—	0.2
2. English	13,984	4.1	16.6	42.0	34.2	2.9	0.1	—
3. Latin	94	19.1	44.7	20.2	13.8	2.1	—	—
4. Greek	2	100.0	—	—	—	—	—	—
5. French	9,570	4.2	20.2	41.0	30.8	3.7	0.1	—
6. German	1,670	8.6	30.2	36.0	23.2	1.9	0.1	—
7. Italian	46	13.0	23.9	26.1	23.9	13.0	—	—
8. Spanish	422	17.1	17.3	36.5	26.3	2.8	—	—
9. History	3,317	7.0	20.6	34.1	26.3	9.0	2.5	0.5
10. Geography	5,059	3.0	14.2	41.3	34.5	6.4	0.5	0.1
11. Mathematics	2,419	3.9	26.4	38.9	26.2	4.1	0.5	0.1
12. Applied Mathematics	101	14.9	25.7	22.8	26.7	9.9	—	—
13. Physics	1,909	5.1	34.9	27.6	23.4	6.8	2.1	0.1
14. Chemistry	3,011	4.5	22.1	32.1	27.0	11.8	2.4	0.1
15. Physics & Chemistry	462	7.1	27.1	28.4	26.2	10.0	1.1	0.2
16. Biology	10,515	3.3	23.2	38.6	25.3	8.2	1.3	0.1
17. Agricultural Science	144	2.8	19.4	49.3	25.0	2.8	0.7	—
18. Agricultural Economics	24	8.3	25.0	45.8	20.8	—	—	—
19. Home Economics (Scientific & Social)	10,086	5.2	23.0	38.5	28.0	4.8	0.5	—
20. Home Economics (General)	614	4.1	13.5	35.2	39.6	6.4	1.1	0.2
21. Accounting	4,402	3.6	26.3	34.6	24.8	8.4	2.1	0.2
22. Business Organisation	6,026	2.9	16.5	32.8	35.4	10.0	2.2	0.2
23. Economics	1,366	5.0	20.7	30.7	27.9	11.4	3.9	0.4
24. Economic History	13	15.4	30.8	46.2	7.7	—	—	—
25. Art	3,668	2.4	15.2	42.4	34.1	5.3	0.6	—
26. Music & Musicianship - A	246	1.6	2.0	27.2	61.8	7.3	—	—
27. Music & Musicianship - B	529	3.6	19.5	51.2	25.1	0.6	—	—
28. Engineering	28	—	28.6	53.6	17.9	—	—	—
29. Technical Drawing	85	4.7	16.5	34.1	32.9	11.8	—	—
30. Construction Studies	43	2.3	25.6	53.5	18.6	—	—	—
31. Hebrew	6	—	50.0	50.0	—	—	—	—
32. Classical Studies	67	1.5	29.9	43.3	23.9	1.5	—	—

*Data refer to School Candidates only

151

APPENDIX TABLE A9

INTERMEDIATE CERTIFICATE EXAMINATION

1975/1983
Percentage of Candidates Passing Mathematics with
Honours in the year specified

YEAR	FEMALE	MALE
1975	11.8	20.3
1976	10.7	17.2
1977	13.1	19.4
1978	15.0	22.2
1979	12.8	19.6
1980	15.7	23.1
1981	*	*
1982	*	*
1983	14.1	20.4

Source: Carey (1990: 46)
        * = Statistics not available.

APPENDIX TABLE A10

LEAVING CERTIFICATE EXAMINATION 1975-1983
Performance of Candidates in Mathematics
Percentage Passed with Honours

YEAR	FEMALE	MALE
1975	2.4	11.5
1976	6.9	10.6
1977	2.5	9.3
1978	2.0	7.9
1979	1.8	7.6
1980	3.5	11.9
1981	*	*
1982	*	*
1983	4.1	10.9

Source: Carey (1990: 51)
        * = Statistics not available

CHAPTER SEVEN

The Netherlands

Truus Dekker
Marja Meeder
Marian Kollenveld

Introduction

All three authors are members of the Dutch 'Women and Mathematics' group which started work in 1981. W&M feels it is very important to have members working at the institutes concerned with mathematics education. This means we are inspired both by the ideas of W&M and the recent developments in mathematics education in the Netherlands as set in motion by institutes like the Freudenthal Institute. This may sometimes mean that on the one hand we describe new developments in mathematics education in which we are ourselves involved and on the other hand criticise the effects for girls of the same developments if we look at them with a 'W&M'-eye.

The Dutch school system

Compulsory schooling in The Netherlands starts at the age of four and ends at the age of 16. No school fee is required during this period. All children have to attend primary school from the age 4-12. During primary education pupils are promoted to the next grade at the end of each year; during secondary education pupils may be obliged to do a certain grade for a second time if their results are unsatisfactory.

At the end of the primary school a choice for secondary education has to be made. In this process of choice two things are important: the teacher's impression of the child's possibilities and the results of a test that is taken by the pupils. In principle all types of schools are co-educational in The Netherlands. However, in practice there are, on the level of lower vocational education, schools attended mostly by boys (technical and nautical education) and schools almost only attended by girls (service and home economics).

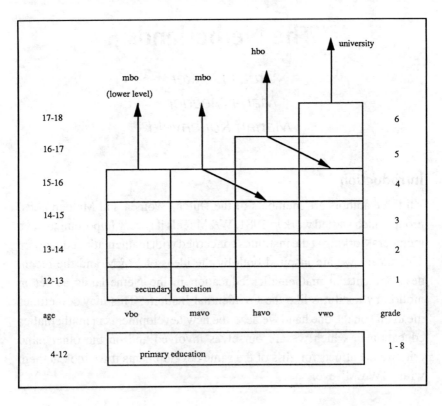

Figure 1: *an overview of the various types of schools providing secondary education in The Netherlands*

In secondary education there are different tracks or streams the choice of which is dictated by the perceived abilities of the student. These tracks are called:

vbo   four year course in vocational education, leading to intermediate vocational education (at a low level) or to the labour market;

mavo   four year course in general education, admission to intermediate vocational education;

havo   five year course granting admission to higher vocational education;

vwo   six year pre-university course.

About 20% of primary school students go on to vbo (lowest level), 70% to general secondary education at mavo, havo and vwo (ascending levels) and 10% attend schools for special education.

The acquired diploma of a certain school type gives the student the right to attend vocational schools or university (see figure 1 above). So there is no system of examinations for admission to a university for example. But for different subjects of advanced studies, certain sets of subjects are necessary. So choosing a set of subjects at the secondary school influences the choice you can make for subjects at the university or higher vocational schools. Without having taken mathematics as a final subject at vwo your directions at university are restricted, for example to (foreign) languages.

In the academic year 1993/94 'basisvorming' (basic educational programme) was introduced in all schools. During basisvorming all students take the same set of fifteen subjects of which mathematics is important. One purpose of introducing basisvorming is to improve the general level of education; another purpose is to have all students aim for the same set of goals for the different subjects. The educational concept of basisvorming is sometimes understood by the three words: applicability, skills, cohesion. Though students may aim at the same goals in basisvorming, they may do so on different levels. Also the period of basisvorming may vary for different students from two to four years. There is no final examination in basisvorming; standardised national examinations for the different tracks of education will still exist.

Freedom of education is considered to be of great importance in the Netherlands. Choice is the key word in the Dutch school system.

- Schools are free to choose the number of lessons per subject. They may choose the curriculum and even, during basisvorming, the grade in which certain subjects are taught.

- Teachers choose their own textbook. They are responsible for tests given to their pupils.

- Pupils and their parents have freedom of choice of the school type after primary education and of the school itself they want to attend. Pupils choose their set of subjects for the final examinations and, at the upper grades of havo/vwo, between different mathematics curricula.

The final examinations for the different types of schools, however, are standardised and equal for all pupils at a certain level.

Freedom of choice in our educational system is certainly worthwhile but making choices implies there is a possibility of making the wrong choice. We feel that girls often 'stay on the safe side' and let themselves be guided more by 'liking' than by 'needing' and are in effect encouraged to do so. In choosing the level of education this sometimes means girls do not choose to match their abilities. We find more boys than girls at the highest and lowest level of secondary education (vbo and vwo) and more girls than boys at the levels in between (mavo and havo).

Final examinations

During a week in May all students of the last grade of mavo-, havo- and vwo-schools in the Netherlands are busy doing their final examinations, at the same time and according to the type of school, with the same test (see figure 2). Each student has the right to have a re-examination in one subject in the same period.

The examination consists of two parts. One is a set of school tests for the final year, composed by the teacher herself and the other one is the standardised, national, written test. At vbo- level some students take the same final examination as mavo- students but the majority of vbo-pupils complete their schooling by taking an internal examination with a rather low status.

Figure 2: *standardised national examinations*

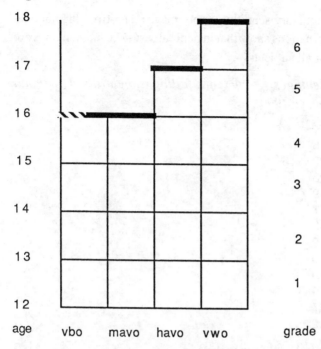

The students' papers are marked by their own teachers, according to the norm that was sent with the examinations. A second opinion is obtained from a teacher of another school. In order to decide whether the results of a student in some subject are sufficient, two marks are important. First the average mark of the tests taken during the final school year. And second, the results of the national examination in the subject. The average of both makes up the final mark for a subject on a 1 to 10-scale.

The composition of the final examinations is the responsibility of CITO, the national institute for assessment. The ministry of education is the principal. The problems and questions for the examinations are designed by a group of teachers from the school type concerned under guidance of a CITO-representative. Until 1993, vbo/mavo examinations in mathematics consisted of both multiple-choice and open problems, each 50%. However, a new examination programme for mavo/vbo has been introduced and there will be a change in these examinations from 1997. For havo and vwo there will be no multiple-choice questions in mathematics.

Achievement at the standardised national examination

At the end of compulsory schooling (vbo, mavo) data from the national standardised examinations show that in general results in mathematics are often the lowest of all subjects:

Figure 3: *Percentages of students failing standardised national examination vbo/mavo 1990*

	%
Dutch	16
French	20
German	23
English	19
Spanish	27
Mathematics	42
Physics	29
Chemistry	30
Biology	19
Economy	14
Geology	27
History	12

Source: CBS (Central statistical office)

The results at havo and vwo show a comparable image, the failure rates for mathematics being the worst. We think this is an unsatisfying result of all the strain of trying to learn mathematics. Beside that, it supplies an affirmation of the idea of mathematics being difficult and hard to learn.

Mathematics in the different tracks

As already stated, at the end of primary school parents and their children choose a comprehensive school, out of a range of school types and streams. Or they may prefer a small school with only one type of secondary schooling, for example vbo, lower vocational education. At the same time as basisvorming was introduced, the ministry of education encouraged the development of large comprehensive schools. The consequences of this cannot yet be predicted but it is clear there will be many changes in the next few years.

Vbo

At the present time, this type of education is seen to be appropriate to technical, agricultural, administrative or home economics education both in terms of its level and the vocational type (see Figure 4).

total		agricultural	nautical technical	service home economics	economic administrative
boys	43,000	4,000	33,000	1,000	5,000
girls	29,000	2,000	2,000	18,000	7,000
total	72,000	6,000	35,000	19,000	12,000

Figure 4: nautical/technical schools are almost completely boys schools, service/home-economics are almost completely girls schools. data about 72.000 vbo graduates in 1991

source: CBS (Central Statistical Office)

After the period of basisvorming vbo-pupils have to choose six subjects including Dutch and one foreign language (mostly English). Four subjects are optional, including the vocational ones. Once the choice for lower vocational education is made it is difficult to make the step from this type of school to a higher level of general education. However there is a good chance to study the same vocational direction at a higher level.

Not all vbo-students take mathematics as an examination subject; it is only compulsory during the period of basisvorming.

Mavo

Like vbo-students pupils at mavo choose their set of examination subjects after the period of basisvorming. Though the number of girls taking mathematics as an examination subject is increasing at the present time, more boys choose mathematics.

Both the students and their parents are assisted in making their choice by a vocational advisor. But of course others (teachers, classmates) have a great deal of influence on the decisions made by a student regarding her or his choice of examination subjects and level.

The choice whether or not to take mathematics as an examination subject is made at the age of 14-15, at the same time as puberty-influences

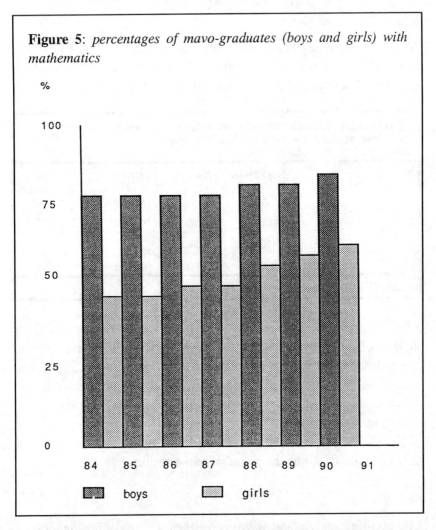

Figure 5: *percentages of mavo-graduates (boys and girls) with mathematics*

are very strong. Girls have to meet a double standard at that age. They are expected to do well at school. But they also should do well socially, have boyfriends and be popular among classmates. Their marks in mathematics tend to drop drastically in this period.

If the marks they got in mathematics are not very high during the first school years, girls will hesitate to take mathematics as an examination subject and are not encouraged to do so. They might say: 'Well, mathematics is too difficult for me.' With the same or even worse results boys tend to take mathematics as an examination subject saying: 'It is important for my future.' (See Figure 5).

The Dutch school system surely provides much freedom as it offers many moments of free choice for both the students and their parents. But this is not always to the benefit of girls.

Havo/Vwo

At havo/vwo the choice whether or not to take mathematics as an examination subject is made in grade 3/4, at the age of 15-16.

In 1985 in vwo, pre-university education, two new programmes for mathematics were introduced, mathematics A and B. As an examination subject students may choose either mathematics A or mathematics B, both mathematics A and mathematics B or no mathematics at all.

Mathematics B is predominantly pure mathematics, with an emphasis on functions and graphs rather then on strong algebraic manipulations. In three dimensional geometry the problems arise from rather technical fields. It is often used in applications such as architecture, and sometimes art. In mathematics A, the techniques are used in relation to real life problems chosen from fields like economics, biology or geography.

Some data are already available regarding the influence of the new mathematics A and B programmes on the choices made by boys and girls. The positive side is that, since the introduction of the new programmes, more students are choosing mathematics as an examination subject, the percentage of students who do not choose mathematics having decreased:

— boys from around 20% to less than 10%

— girls from around 40% to around 20%

Students also show more enjoyment in the new mathematics A and B than was apparent in the previous programme.

The negative side is that mathematics B, which is necessary for pursuing technical or scientific further education, is now chosen less often than was its counterpart in the previous programme:

— boys from 80% to 60%

— girls from 60% to 30%

There follows an overview of percentages of vwo-students choosing mathematics as an examination subject:

Figure 6: percentages of all vwo-students with mathematics A and mathematics B								
havo					vwo			
year	1986	1991	1993			1987	1990	1993
girls	45	57	math A	56	math A	55	59	63
			math B	18	math B	30	31	31
boys	75	77	math A	46	math A	62	63	58
			math B	47	math B	64	61	63

In 1990 in havo, as in vwo, two new programmes, mathematics A and B were also introduced. The same effects, but more strongly, on the choices of boys and girls have appeared at this type of school.

Choosing mathematics B at havo or vwo often means to choose being in a 'boys-only' class. Which girl of 16 can afford to say she would like that? Not choosing mathematics as an examination subject means you have no possibilities to enter certain vocational schools or university studies. In practice this might mean students have chosen school careers without much hope of finding a job. Without mathematics many directions are closed. Sometimes there are ways to have a second chance to make up the mathematics which is lacking but these are expensive, complex or just too late. In this way mathematics is used as a selective device.

Freedom of choice in our educational system, especially for girls may lead to a 'cul-de-sac' where mathematics is concerned.

Content of the mathematics programme

Much has changed in recent years in mathematics education in the Netherlands. In primary schools (age four to twelve) more and more of the textbooks used are based on a new vision of mathematics education entailing a shift from mechanistic to 'realistic' mathematics. This does not always mean that teachers are teaching in an appropriate style. The change that took place is visual in the content of the textbooks.

As already indicated, two new mathematics programmes were introduced into the last two years of vwo in 1985 and havo in 1990. These programmes, mathematics A and mathematics B, replaced the single existing mathematics programme. The missing link in the process to revamp mathematics at all levels was the mathematics programme for 12 to 16 year olds. The new programme for these students was introduced in all schools in the 1993/94 academic year at the same time as basisvorming.

In the development of this new programme, the ministry of education specifically required that the demands of mathematics education for girls be met. It was therefore possible to request the appointment of women to the development group and involve W&M in devising the course.

The introduction of new programmes in all types of schools has been a 'mathematics for all' approach. This does not mean that all students learn the same mathematics. Choice of subject matter varies with the type of school. The emphasis with vbo-students lies strongly on using mathematics in everyday life and work, while, with vwo-students, the subject matter supports the more formal mathematics necessary for university education. At all levels, learning with the aid of contexts plays an important role.

In general more demands are placed on the applicability of mathematics and on its relevance for the student in her or his future life. Mathematics is becoming a subject that primarily supplies students with the knowledge and skills they need in everyday life and their chosen profession. More than was the case in the past, the subject matter of mathematics education is now attuned to practical uses. Less attention is now paid to 'math for math's sake'.

This renovated mathematics education can be characterised by the use of contexts. Through working with contexts, a link can be made with what the students already know; in addition, mathematics is seen to be applicable in a wide range of situations. The contexts used are taken from as many areas of interest to the students as possible. Questions should be asked to fit the context, not contexts chosen to fit certain questions. This is related to the respect for the common sense of the students. Manipulation with a context in order to frame mathematical content and to leave out all other aspects is seen to be counterproductive. But of course contexts are no purpose in themselves. Using contexts means making explicit the mathematical content. There have to be moments of vertical mathematisation, resulting in developing tools that can be used to solve other problems, such tools as graphs, formula and their manipulation, geometrical concepts etc. On the other hand it is important to compare the results of applying the mathematical model with the context which led to its derivation.

New examination for vbo/mavo

The revamping of the mathematics programme for the first phase of secondary education has been in progress since 1988. For vbo and mavo this includes a new examination programme. It is not the intention to introduce two separate programmes, mathematics A and B, into the first phase of secondary education. Since the new mathematics curriculum was only introduced in 1993, the first national examination will take place in 1997. This too, consists of a number of internal examinations and a standardised national examination.

Because of the freedom in the years up to the final examinations, standardised national examinations are an important instrument in the process of changing the curriculum. Showing new material resources for students is useful, as are the first drafts of the proposed programme especially for publishers. But the strongest influence on teachers is to show the proposed examinations. Sentences in a programme come alive if you can show an appropriate problem in the examination with details of how students performed. You address the teachers' confidence directly, giving an idea about the level of the examination, so that they can imagine what their own students would do with this particular problem. Experimental examinations enable teachers to express whether or not they agree with new developments.Therefore the commission in charge of making the new mathematics programme for 12-16, (COW), co-operated with CITO, the national institute for assessment, in order to be able to produce a new national examination at the level of vbo/mavo which would fit the new programme. A few characteristics of this experimental examination are:

School tests

The school tests during the final school year, taken at the schools participating in the experimental examination, were different from what is customary. Although the schools are free here to do as they please, school tests at most schools are currently a reflection of the standardised national examination. The experimental internal examinations provided experience in other ways of testing.

• *Oral instead of written examination*

The questions were more or less comparable with those on a written examination, but students who got stuck could be given a small clue. And, of course, some students are better able to express themselves verbally than in writing.

• *Oral examination in connection with a project or free assignment*

Students could work independently on the project throughout the examination year, either alone or in small groups. Questions regarding this project were asked during the internal examination.

Standardised national examination

• *No multiple-choice questions*

Multiple choice questions have no place in an examination consisting of context questions. The point of departure in designing the experimental examination was that the emphasis should lie on providing good argument. The answers are not unequivocal and the students need not follow anyone else's thought processes. Analysis of the results of the traditional examination revealed that, on the whole, girls do worse on multiple-choice questions than do boys.

• *Avoiding command language*

In posing questions care is taken to avoid command language such as 'write down' or 'calculate'. Everyday language is used as much as possible. Naturally, a compromise must continually be made between a mathematically correct formulation and one that is comprehensible to the students.

• *Mathematics in recognisable situations*

A great deal of attention is paid to using mathematics in recognisable situations familiar to the students, as suggested by a newspaper clipping for instance.

• *Making assumptions*

Sometimes it is necessary for a student to make certain assumptions (and to make them explicit by writing them down!) because of the model being used or because the student failed to answer a former question. These are demands which are important for future life, either as a reader of newspapers or in a profession.

In addition, the order of magnitude in which the answer is to be given and the indication of size must sometimes be chosen by the student. For the students this often is not easy. Girls in particular must develop the ability to take risks and dare to make an estimate or to round off.

- *Available time*

An attempt was made to ensure that the students would not run out of time. In spite of this, some students were busy right up to the end of the allotted time. The teachers were under the impression that girls in particular were less apt to take risks and also spent more time with a question they were not able to figure out. Open questions can in fact be to their disadvantage!

By posing questions in what may or may not be a mathematical context, a greater appeal is made to the students' language skills. This may prove to be a problem for certain groups of students, such as those using Dutch as a second language.

The questions asked in these experimental examinations were published yearly because nationally organised examinations are considered of great importance in the Netherlands. Therefore this was an important strategy to communicate the change of the curriculum to a wide public.

Assessment

During the period of compulsory schooling, as well as the examinations, there are two other moments of assessment for all students.

At the end of primary education (age 12)

At the end of the primary school all pupils take a test. The school is free to choose a test-institute and the results of the test are merely used in order to give advice as to which school is appropriate for secondary education. Many schools use the so called CITO-toets from the national institute for assessment. Some schools train their pupils in order to get better results, other schools just arrange for the test to take place and do no more. Some pupils see the test as a kind of examination but the influence of the results of the test are not too great, the advice of the child's teacher being as important.

In 1987 a national gauge concerning the level of education in arithmetic at the end of primary school was held (PPON).This showed considerable difference in achievement of arithmetic between girls and boys. In general boys did better than girls though there were differences in fields like applicability (boys did better) or plain ciphering and measurement (girls did better). No explanation for these differences in achievement was offered. Far more boys than girls at primary level attend schools for special education and these schools were left out of the investigation which could have influenced the results.

After basisvorming

Because basisvorming was introduced in 1993, no assessment of the goals of this basic education has yet taken place. Presumably all students will have to take a test, comparable to the CITO-test for primary education already mentioned. Discussion about the content of the test is still going on. It is now clear that the test at the end of basisvorming will also make use of contexts.

During secondary schooling

During secondary schooling teachers are free to make their own tests and free to choose the mode of assessment being used. In general for mathematics these tests are written and done by all students at the same time. The questions asked are similar to those posed in the textbooks. Oral assessment, groupwork, homework assignments, doing a project are not common in our schools though each teacher could choose to use these styles. Tradition is still strong!

Commercial editors of textbooks sometimes provide tests to fit their books. To use alternative ways of finding out the possibilities of a student is rare. At the end of the school year all teachers award marks in their subject and decide whether the student may pass to the next grade.

Concluding summary

The Dutch school system

An overview of the Dutch school system has displayed its complexity. For parents it is often difficult to find their way in this labyrinth. Characteristic of this system is freedom of choice. For girls especially, this may have great consequences.

- Girls too often choose tracks or subjects which are not helpful to finding a job afterwards.
- Girls tend to choose according to their interests and not their abilities.

Final examinations

Because of the freedom of education, standardised national examinations play an important role in the implementation of the new curriculum. Achievements in mathematics in the national examinations are often the worst of all subjects.

Mathematics in the different tracks

At all school types of secondary school students have to choose whether or not to take mathematics as an examination subject. At havo and vwo they have to choose between mathematics A and mathematics B.

Even if they achieve good marks for mathematics, girls hesitate to choose mathematics as an examination subject and in this way close possibilities for further studies.

Contents of the mathematics programme

The changes in the mathematics curriculum emphasise the importance of practical, applicable knowledge and abilities. In learning mathematics contexts play an important role. We feel that this is important for both girls and boys.

- Contexts used in mathematics should be chosen very carefully and appeal to both girls and boys. Students with a large diversity of experiences and interest should find learning mathematics easier possible by the use of these contexts.
- The use of contexts makes an integrative educational appeal and includes knowledge acquired outside the school. Teachers must be prepared to handle this.

Assessment

During the period of compulsory schooling (4-16) there are two moments of assessing the achievements of all students, at the end of primary school and at the end of 'basisvorming' (basic education).

- The Dutch school system has no formal barriers to use different modes or styles of assessment during secondary education and in internal examinations.

- It is new to acknowledge that being able to 'talk about mathematics', and use your creative talents, for example when doing a project, are important mathematical capabilities.

Note

1 All data in this chapter come from the Central Statistical Office, Voorburg, except for figure 6 page 115 where the 1993 data were supplied by CITO, the national institute for assessment.

References

Anon (1993) B-examendundel, vbo. APS Utrecht.

Anon (1992) Achtergronden van het nieuwe leerplan wiskunde, band 1 en 2, Freudenthal instituut Utrecht/SLO Enschede.

Anon (1992) Trajectenboek wiskunde 12-16. Freudenthal instituut Utrecht/SLO Enschede.

Brink, J. van den (1993), Different aspects in designing mathematics education: three examples from the Freudenthal institute, Educational studies in Mathematics (24) 195-214.

Dekker, T. (1993) De basisvorming getoetst, Nieuwe Wiskrant 13 (2) 5-9.

Dekker, T. (1990, 1991, 1992) Examenbundel vbo/mavo C/D Educaboek Culemborg.

Lange, J. de (1993) Assessment in problem-orientated curricula, In: N. Webb and A. Coxford. Assessment in the mathematics classroom. NCTM 1993 Yearbook, 197-209.

Linden J. van der, I. de Vet, L. Schepers en H. Verhage (1993) Wiskunde en werk. Stichting Vrouwen en Exacte Vakken, Utrecht.

Meeder M., F. Meester, R. Dekker, C. Geijsel en Th. de Poel (1984) Vrouwiskundig Stichting Vrouwen en Exacte Vakken, Utrecht.

Meeder M., F. Meester (1990) .... erbij blijven. Begeleiden motiveren en adviseren in de wiskundeles. VU-uitgeverij, Amsterdam.

Meeder M., F. Meester, J. van Dormolen, G. Gorter en B. Lagerwery (1991) Emancipatie abc voor de wiskundeles. Hogeschool Holland, Diemen.

Meeder M., F. Meester en H. Verhage (1987) Vriendelijke wiskunde. Stichting Vrouwen en Exacte Vakken, Utrecht.

Spijkerboer L. (1993) Toetsen van realistisch wiskundeonderwijs, Nieuwe Wiskrant 12 (2) 25-30.

Werf S. van der (1989) Wiskunde in het LHNO, logisch toch! Stichting Vrouwen en Exacte Vakken, Utrecht.

CHAPTER EIGHT

Norway

Liv Berge
Monica Varøy Haga

We begin with a description of Norwegian educational policy and reforms within the school system as a base from which to understand the current assessment debate. School has been an important arena for moves against gender discrimination, important decisions have been taken, and a lot of effort has been spent in giving boys and girls the same rights and opportunities. The section is concluded with an outline of the current debate on education policy in Norway, and some of the plans made for future changes in the school system.

In the section headed General Assessment Debate, we describe the tests used and system of examinations installed by central authorities, and the debate concerning testing as a means of measuring qualities in the school system. We refer to the debate on marks and the use of marks which is the basis for questions on the role of assessment in secondary school. The ongoing struggle to make the school system more efficient is described and so is the work done in government-appointed projects, looking at assessment and guidance, organisation and management in the educational sector.

In the section Assessment, Mathematics and Gender, we give a short summary on the use of tests in compulsory school and analyse results of research done. The lack of statistical data in general, and especially gender differentiated data, is noted. A summary of individual projects done on the subject of gender and mathematics in the late 1970s and the beginning of the 1980s is included. Questions are asked as to why so little work has been done on this issue since then. The section concludes with a short summary of work in progress on gender and mathematics by one of the authors.

Educational Policy in Norway

The last few decades in Norwegian education have been characterised by rapid expansion in participation at the post-compulsory levels and by extensive structural diversification. The expansion has often been described as a transition from elite to mass education, promoting higher rates of participation beyond the compulsory school, Grunnskule (7-16). (A description of the existing Norwegian education system is given in Appendix 1.) Educational activities already in existence have undergone profound changes, and many new activities have been established. In recent years a debate on future educational policy has arisen. There follows the background for it, together with a brief summary.

Educational policy in Norway after the Second World War can roughly be divided into four main phases. From 1945 to the middle of the 1960s the political focus was on expansion of the system, with equal educational opportunities for all as the main aim. In this phase the idea to use educational policy as an instrument, among others, to create the welfare state, was developed. From 1947 state financial support was available for students. School was compulsory for pupils aged 7 to 14, as it had been from the 1920s. The school system continued to be strongly centralised in this period, regulated through two National Curricula, one for rural areas, one for urban areas.

It was not until 1959 that girls and boys formally got the same rights in school. Pupils from rural and urban areas had different allocations of teaching periods. In rural areas pupils had the same number of lessons in mathematics. But in urban areas boys had 2 more lessons a week in mathematics than girls. In the textbooks some of the problems were marked by a little asterisk to show that these problems were meant only for the boys to solve, the asterisk gave the pupils a clear signal that these problems were too difficult for girls. Girls had home economics and nursery subjects when boys were taught solid geometry. After compulsory school, boys and girls were to compete on equal terms for the right to study science in junior forms at grammar school; later in the science branch. This gave the boys a great advantage. Furthermore, these quantitative reforms were accompanied by important qualitative policies on science and mathematics, initiated by OECD (1959), and furthered by a joint committee (1960) in the Nordic countries. (Solvang, 1986)

In this period assessment was school-based up to the 7th grade; the teachers were expected to award marks twice a year on a five point scale, at every level in school. Examinations for all pupils were held at the end of 7th grade and were under the control of central authorities.

The 2nd phase, mid 60s to mid 70s, still meant a strong quantitative growth, but was also marked by fundamental *reforms in the structure* of the educational system. Compulsory school was extended to 9 years, now including the primary school (grades 1-6) and lower secondary school (grades 7-9). This was regulated through the Educational Act of 1969. In 1974 a new, and radically changed curriculum was introduced. Compared to the old curriculum the new National Curriculum Guidelines for compulsory school (M74), established a binding framework, and should be considered as a source of ideas and inspiration to the teachers, schools and local authorities. These guidelines included, among other new issues, a whole chapter dealing with gender equality. M74 rearranged and changed some of the subjects, introducing some new teaching methods like co-operation and groupwork. Effectively, M74 led to a drive towards decentralisation of education authorities and opened the possibilities of developing local curricula. M74 had as a higher objective that the teaching should be adapted to the abilities of each pupil. Another important goal for educational policy in this decade was to make upper secondary education available for all, regulated by the Upper Secondary Act of 1974. In principle, this new secondary school was open to every student who had completed basic education, an important step away from elite education.

The new syllabus in mathematics (1974) was only partly built on the research projects done on modern mathematics initiated by the Nordic committee in the 60s. In 1972 an extensive discussion and criticism of 'modern mathematics' in school started. This criticism influenced the new syllabus in mathematics in M74. (Solvang, 1986)

In this period the debate on assessment started. Assessment came to mean more than just the discussion of which scale of marks to use, test, number and forms of examinations. It was broadened to include the discussion of the ideologies surrounding the process of education. This topic will be discussed further in a later section (General Assessment Debate). In 1974 the use of school-based marks up to 7th grade was abandoned and the evaluation of each child was done informally, based on oral as well as written evidence.

In the 3rd phase, mid 70s to mid 80s, some new topics emerged on the policy agenda including decentralisation, curricular content and control of education. The work with local curricula started up on a significant level in various municipalities. In addition to this, the work on school innovation included development of methods for project work as a learning style. The preparation for new curriculum guidelines was started in this phase. The Council of Primary and Lower Secondary Education was asked to prepare a draft document for the general and subject related parts of the curriculum guidelines. Arising from this and the related debates, a new curricular guide was published in 1987 (M87). Despite major submissions on gender equality this 1987 document included no major advance on the topic. Although M87 proposed welcome policy shifts on curricular philosophy, objectives and local content, it did not propose any big changes in the syllabus of mathematics, and no changes relating to mathematics and gender. M87 records that each school should work out a local curriculum, taking the environment and the pupils' background into account.

At the beginning of this phase, mid 1980s, the evaluation of children in primary went through a change. The teachers were to evaluate each child individually, to inform the pupils and their parents about their progress, or lack of progress, in a way which would inspire and guide the pupils in their further work. This was done both orally and in writing. By M87 evaluation in primary school was changed again. Evaluation should be in the same spirit as earlier, but it should either take place as a meeting between parents, teacher and pupil or by means of written reports. In addition to this a strengthening of school assessment was entered into the curriculum, as well as the wish to include the pupils in the general assessment of work in school.

The last phase, from mid 1980s until now is characterised by a stronger demand from various parts of society to exercise influence on schools. This phase provoked some clashes of interests, the idea of centralisation against the idea of decentralisation, control against freedom, economic restriction against use of money to develop the school system further. From 1987 a new sector grant system was introduced. This meant a trend towards greater decentralisation of educational authorities, from the Ministry to the regional or local educational authorities. The counties and municipalities have greater influence on how sums of money, allocated by Parliament, are to be spent.

In 1987, OECD, continuing its series of country studies initiated as the Education Investment Project (EIP) in 1962, conducted a systematic review of the Norwegian education system. Their report, *Review of National Policies for Education in Norway* (1987), later in this paper referred to as 'the 1987 OECD report', has been used as support for a demand for more efficiency, central accountability and stronger centralisation of school authorities. Too often, education and schools are seen as manipulative agents of society. For trade and industry and for parts of the political system, or state bureaucracy and departments, school is frequently seen as a tool to help solve the problems caused by unemployment and economic depression. Their view seems to be that a good educational system, and a high level of knowledge will increase the ability to compete technically and economically with other countries. In connection with this, there are some key questions being asked but not answered: What is a good school system? What is knowledge? What kind of knowledge do we need? This has been an issue for broad discussion, at the end of the 1980s in Norway (e.g. Mellin-Olsen, 1989).

In a White Paper nr.37 (1990-91), *Concerning organisation and management in the education sector*, it is stated:

> The main tools available to central government for national control of the education system are acts and regulations, curricula, evaluation and feedback, training for school heads, teacher training, centrally co-ordinated research and development work, and financing. The use of economic sanctions to penalise county and municipal authorities

that have not fulfilled their statutory obligations will have to be considered. (p.5)

If such policies are fully implemented it means that the era of decentralisation has come to an end and that central authorities seek to regain the control lost in the process of decentralisation.

In Norway, there existed until recently some independent advisory councils dealing with compulsory and upper secondary school education policy, such as 'The Council for Primary and Lower Secondary Education' (GSR) and 'The Council for Upper Secondary Education' (RVO). The OECD team focused generally on the lack of governance in the Norwegian educational system. Among other critical questions asked was that of the function of these independent councils. The OECD experts raised the possibility for specialists in the Councils to have opinions diverging from those the government holds, and that it would be difficult to reconcile them with the wish from central authorities to have control and governance. As a consequence the councils were dismantled and instead some secretariats controlled more directly by government were set up. (St.meld. nr.37 1990-91)

The upper secondary school is now going through some fundamental changes both in structure and content (Reform 94). It is planned that education at this level will be regulated by one comprehensive act which will co-ordinate all vocational training and general education in a comprehensive secondary school. The main intention in this law is to give equal status to practical and theoretical education, and contractual apprenticeship as a part of the ordinary school system. In upper secondary education priority is given to handicapped students, adapting their training to their skills and qualifications...From 1994 everybody leaving compulsory school will be entitled to at least 3 years of secondary education. As a consequence of this change in structure new curricula and syllabuses are under development. A main idea is to make common National Curriculum Guidelines for both compulsory school and upper secondary school.

In Norway the struggle against gender discrimination has to a certain degree been fought through legislation. In the 1970s this led to the establishing of an administrative structure for handling problems related to gender discrimination and gender equality.

The curriculum guidelines of 1974 (M74) stated that teaching aids were not allowed to give single sex applicable, biased or discriminating descriptions of the distribution of work and tasks among the sexes. Teaching aids should give realistic and varied patterns of identification for both girls and boys. Unfortunately very few significant results came out of these statements. An extensive discussion in the 70s on women's position in society, led to the Act on gender equality in 1979 and to the creation of the post of Ombudsman responsible for issues such as gender equality and discrimination, and at a Board of Appeal for gender equality. The statement in the Curriculum Guidelines of 1974 (M74), and one section on 'teaching aids' in the Act on gender equality of 1979, were reactions to years of biased books being used in education. Many books prescribed for education made women invisible, or placed them in the background as waitresses, nurses or mothers.

In mathematics and the natural sciences the female sex was absent with the exception of Marie Curie. All examples used in science subjects and mathematics had been collected from boys' fields of interests and everyday life. It was found important that the books used should not have an imbalance of males and male activities. Girls need, in the same way as boys, someone to take after, persons from whom to get inspiration and take as models. The law does not prevent publishers or authors from making books which are gender discriminatory. It is the schools that are not allowed to use such books. *Every* book used in education is to be read and approved by consultants from the Ministry...This is to ensure that books used do not contain discriminating statements of gender, religion or race. Every second year an award is given to the author of a textbook, who has found a fresh way to fight for gender equality, or a new angle to the subject. The award was established by the Association of Norwegian Non-fiction Writers, the Ministry of Church, Science and Education and the Association of Norwegian Publishers and is meant to stimulate a new drive in the area of equality. In addition action programmes for equality have provided a basis for more systematic efforts toward real equality. In 1981 a White Paper to the Storting presented such an action programme for the forthcoming four years. This was succeeded by a new one in 1985. In the field of education these action programmes focused on teacher training, so the teachers should be able to handle questions relating to gender equality in education and society. Courses and information material were developed, aimed at motivating women to apply for leading positions in the school system.

The idea of equality has had a profound impact on political discussion about change in the educational system. But in spite of the idea of equal opportunities regardless of social background, region and gender, there still exist great educational inequalities connected to gender, region and social background. These inequalities have increased rather than decreased in the 1980s.

Research in the middle 1970s showed a certain success for the social democratic emphasis on equality across social class and geographical regions. Lately, however the trend is changing, and in the 1980s, a comparatively smaller number of students from lower income families were entering the public universities. (There are no private universities in Norway.) Recent data also show that fewer students from the peripheral regions enter the national universities. (Ve and Fjelde, 1991:119)

There has been an increasing proportion of women entering education particularly noticeable in higher education, rising from 41% in 1974 to 51% in 1986. However, men and women still choose very different areas of education. Girls are more likely to enter education in health, social work and teacher training, boys in administration, industry, fishery, farming etc. At the universities we find similar inequalities: men are mainly doing the natural, technical and economic sciences, women mainly the social sciences and humanities. The inequalities in the educational system are transmitted into the labour market, where we find that women are mainly occupied in caring professions and education. Compared to other European countries the Norwegian labour market is strongly gender segregated (see Figure 1, page 179).

In this period despite so many official action programmes for equality there have been very few changes in the choice of career. To a certain degree it seems as though the tendency to greater equality has been reversed.

The Norwegian school system has predominantly been a public one. Fundamental criticism has been raised, particularly in the last decade, against the Norwegian school system by both sides of the political spectrum. The consequence of conservative criticism has been the estab-

Figure 1: *Percentage of pupils by field of study and sex, 1978 and 1989.*
From Educational Statistics 1989.

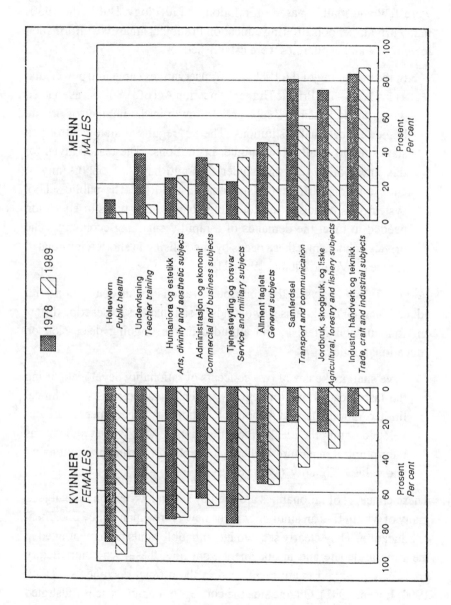

lishment of a private school system side by side with the public school system especially in higher education. Until the 1980s private schools were few and mainly based on religion and ideology. But in the 1980s many private schools offering education in subject areas like information technology and economics were established.

> In the beginning of the 1980s the Conservatives came into power, and a new law — the Private Higher Education Act of 1986 — was enacted which made possible a substantial growth in the number of private higher educational institutions. The act regulated state control and state support to all private higher institutions. The reason given for this new policy was that students should have the opportunity to choose among different educational institutions. The public school system was criticised for not being able to offer types of education needed to meet the demands of a rapidly changing economy. The private schools met these needs by specialising in shorter, job-related courses. (Ve and Fjelde, 1991: 119)

Ve (1989) has analysed the concept of rationality in connection with educational policy. She uses two kinds of rationalities to describe different fundamental interests and attitudes in the ongoing discussion on educational policy.

> .. we shall make use of two concepts of rationality developed during the last decades by Norwegian women social scientists: Technical limited rationality and responsible rationality. The concepts are developed within the ideal-typical tradition of Max Weber, and take as their point of departure Weber's concepts of instrumental rationality and value rationality. (Ve, 1989: 3-4)

These concepts of rationalities are used by several writers on this subject, many of whom find an ambiguity in the new Norwegian policy document of education. They clearly see two incompatible goals both mentioned in the general debate and in documents, but how these two contradictory goals can be united is not mentioned in the official documents. (Tiller, 1990, Imsen, 1991). On one side the concept of competence is illustrated by 'getting enough competence out of the talents in the population' in the framework of economic growth. This competence can be looked upon as an expression of a technically defined limited rationality because talents and competences are considered as means to be used by the country to achieve economic growth. In other words, there is a wish to extract as much knowledge out of the educational system as cheaply as possible and in the shortest time possible. But what kind of knowledge do we need? The concept of knowledge used in the official documents has been criticised by educational commentators (see above). On the other hand it is important to develop the ability of reflection and criticism and to introduce ethics into all subjects of education. One of the aims is to enable the pupils to be critical in the use of modern technology. This is regarded as the rationality of caring and the rationality of responsibility, taking all human aspects into consideration. The problem is how to combine this with economic and technical aims.

General Assessment Debate

Debate on assessment has more or less always been a part of educational policy in Norway. But it was not until the very end of the 1960s and the beginning of the 1970s that the discussion was broadened, to include a more radical criticism of traditional assessment forms and propose new and radical forms of assessments. The official documents being used in the politically changing process of the school system in the 1960s had a very technical and traditional view of assessment. Assessment was mainly synonymous with use of tests and examinations, formal marks and formal exams. Pupils were the ones to be evaluated, evaluation of schools was not part of the agenda. The control and power function which the use of marks and examinations had of pupils and the process of learning were not discussed; neither were the pupils' social background nor gender. The discussion was often limited to which scale of marks should be used.

At the end of the 1960s there was a strong desire to find an equitable and fair way of giving pupils marks. The idea was to find a way to ensure that a specific mark given at one school should be the same as at every school for the same achievement. The ideology underlying the use of marks was not discussed at all. At this stage there was a widespread expectation that an unbiased measure of knowledge could be found and used as a guideline for giving marks. The National Council for Innovation in Education agreed, very strongly, together with Educational Committees appointed by the Government to establish an Assessment of Performance Institute. This Institute was proposed to be in charge of a nation-wide and uniform use of formal tests in school. One of the arguments being used for establishing this Institute was the need for justice in providing information (through formal marks) to different institutions of higher education. (Telhaug, 1979)

In 1969 a debate on the use of standardised and objective tests started. These tests already had a tradition in Norwegian schools, and very few questions about the use of these tests had been asked until the proposal of a test institute. The debate, on-going for several years, included very strong criticism of this style of assessment. The consequence was that the Government (KUD) in 1973 decided not to establish the 'test- institute'. This decision was also influenced by the current debate on the introduction of a new National Curriculum for primary school and lower secondary school, where ideas like decentralised planning for each school and teaching adapted to the abilities of each pupil were important. The introduction of the new National Curriculum (M74) in 1974 also meant an introduction of a new assessment style. From 1974 marks were not used in primary school, grades 1-6, but maintained from grades 7-9 in obligatory subjects. In elective subjects pupils could decide themselves, together with their parents, if marks were to be used or not. At the end of lower secondary school (7-9), there was (and is) a final written examination organised by the central authority.

The politicisation of the assessment debate was also strengthened by the work of a committee appointed by the Government in 1972. The brief given to the committee was to give an evaluation and promote a proposal on the function, form and extent of assessment in primary and secondary schools. Its first report, (EVA I, 1974), was met with a very strong debate involving the whole society. Most people had an opinion on YES or NO to use of marks in school. The majority of the committee went in for the abolition of marks in compulsory school, grades 1-9. The committee members found the use of formal marks incompatible with the aims in the new National Curriculum, like pupil oriented learning with no room for streaming. A minority of the committee members also favoured the abolition of marks in upper secondary school. In the second report from the committee (EVA II, 1977) the majority of its members held on to the idea of not using marks in compulsory school and concluded that many and different sides of the informal assessment system carried out in school ought to be strengthened. According to the committee, it was essential to strengthen school assessment and allow pupils to be a part of the assessment work (Telhaug, 1979). The latter concept has been included in the National Curriculum of Compulsory school (M87).

The debate on assessment continued, but still with the focus very much on the use of marks in school. The result was that the proposal from the committee on new assessment forms was dismissed. It was not until 1983 that a White Paper (St.mld.62(1982-83)) took the matter up again. In this Paper more knowledge of, and research on, assessment in compulsory school was sought, how assessment was practised and which function it had; both informal assessment in grades 1-6 and formal assessment in grades 7-9. It was about the new style of assessment introduced by the National Curriculum of 1974 (M74) that the government was asking for more knowledge in the White Paper of 1983.

In 1986 the National Council of Compulsory School initiated a nation-wide research project on assessment and guidance (St.mld.43.) The aim was to illuminate and further develop both formal and informal assessment:

i)   examining how formal and informal assessment can be used together and complement each other;

ii) trying to find assessment procedure alternatives to the existing ones.

One year after the project had started, in 1988, it was made clear by the Department that the schools were not allowed to develop alternative styles of assessment to the formal ones existing in grades 7-9 of compulsory school, which meant that pupils in the schools connected to the project had to take ordinary examinations arranged by the central authorities. Schools involved in the project found the use of marks to be an obstacle to the local work of school improvement. So the project had to go on without being able to develop better formal styles of assessment (Raaen, 1990).

The report from this project was finished in 1990. Among the main conclusions were:

— great need for systematising and formalising informal assessment,

— need to establish a connection between formal and informal assessment,

— pupils profited by being part of the assessment work,

183

— need to find a connection between assessment and local development of curriculum,

— the project gave little information about gender disparities.

The assessment debate in upper secondary school started much later than
in compulsory school as late as the end of the 1980s. (RVO, 1988), (RVO,
1990), (RVO, 1991). It seems to be much more directed by society in
general, the labour market, business life, trade and industry, unemployment and the problems in the economy. The school is being criticised from
many different sides for not giving the pupils high quality, relevant
knowledge. The authorities want to maximise the return on money spent
on education and not least, it seems, wish to regain the control lost in the
process of decentralisation.

With the 1987 OECD report on the Norwegian school system the
assessment debate seemed to gain a new focus. A main conclusion in the
report is the lack of official assessment systems and control of the whole
educational system. The government initiated a project on the issues of
assessment in compulsory school, called the EMIL-project, a project
which was very different from the former project in compulsory school,
'Assessment and Guidance'. In the final report from EMIL (Granheim
and Lundgren, 1990), terminology from trade and industry like competence and effectiveness, is used frequently; however pedagogical terms
like pupil-oriented learning, local development of curriculum are very
rare. A major issue in this debate concerns a conflict between demands
from society and authorities and the autonomy of pupils, schools and
teachers.

In 1992 the Government appointed a committee to work on assessment
in school including all levels from primary school to upper secondary
school and establish concepts of organisation and management in the
educational sector. This is a consequence of White Paper nr.37 (1990-91)
and the final result of the EMIL project (Granheim and Lundgren, 1990).
The committee is to function for two years, and so far it has come up with
a '5-step-rocket' to establish a system of governance.

1) The Ministry of Education and Research to formulate the objectives
   in such a way that it will be possible to evaluate the results. These
   objectives are to be less general than earlier objectives in legislation

and curriculum guidelines. This leads to a need for new curricula and syllabuses.

2) The whole educational system to be informed about the new objectives.

3) Districts, municipalities and schools are to give the objectives concrete shape.

4) The evaluation of the results is to take place in each class at every school. The purpose of this is to uncover the circumstances impeding the achievement of the objectives. Questions to be asked are of the kind: 'have the expected goals been achieved?' If not — is there anything wrong with the organisation, textbooks, methods used, teachers. Are there other explanations?

5) Response is to be returned to the authorities according to common sense. The authorities are to find out if there is a need for more resources to realise the objectives.

The current assessment debate appears, so far, to be gender 'neutral' which leads us to wonder if the legislation on the subject of gender equality, the campaigns and action programmes have led us to believe that this is no longer a problem in Norwegian schools? As it is not regarded as a problem, questions on gender issues are not asked. The 1987 OECD report has come to play a central part in the assessment debate in Norway, and has influenced the debate more than other documents and is frequently referred to in the debate. The 1987 OECD report does not focus on gender equality as a public problem. It concluded that:

> The official policy is clear enough and institutions are in no doubt about the policy. The problems are now largely those of individual preference, to be tackled at a level of individual counselling and encouragement. (p.29)

Assessment, Mathematics and Gender

In trying to connect the current assessment debate to the assessment of mathematics, we get very little help from the official debate which we have described. In trying to make connections between the current assessment debate and styles of assessment of mathematics with respect to their impact on gender differentiated achievement, we get no help at all, because this has not been a focus of attention. As already mentioned, the few exceptions are Tiller (1990), Imsen (1991) and Monsen and Tiller (1991) who connect the assessment debate to the debate on different types of rationalities developed by women researchers, where the rationality of caring and responsibility is seen in opposition to economic and technical rationality. But this debate has been on a general level and not connected to individual subjects in school, like mathematics. We feel, however, that it is possible to find a way of looking at gender and mathematics in connection with the current debate on assessment and argue for this point of view. But first we will give a short summary of the use of official testing in mathematics. (In Appendix No.2 a summary of assessment forms and allocation of teaching periods in the compulsory school is given.)

Every year, an official regulated test is offered to all lower secondary schools in different subjects, including mathematics. The tests are made and evaluated by the Council of Compulsory School. In mathematics the test is given in grade 7 and grade 9. About 70% of the schools in grade 7 and about 90% in grade 9 do this regulated test. The objective is multi-sectional:

— to be a tool for the teacher in the work of giving marks,

— to ensure that the marks given represent the same skills,

— to introduce and assess new kinds of problems to be solved,

— to test the correlation between the mark given on the test and the average mark based on classwork.

In the beginning the only purpose of the tests was to ensure the unity and equality in evaluation by mark in a national perspective. As the tests and their use have evolved, the goals have expanded. In addition to this the tests have changed according to the different syllabuses and the attaching of importance to other topics. There is a diverging view on the ideology behind the use of these tests. In our opinion the tests are used as an instrument more for governance than for guiding. The official authorities claim that they provide guidance for teachers, and are not a tool for control. In the process of analysing the results of the tests, a sample of the population of pupils is chosen by picking some birthdates at random. The tests are corrected and treated statistically, adjusted to the normal distribution based on the Gaussian curve. For each mark an interval of points is given, and returned to each school. This gives the teachers the possibility to compare their marks with the official standard. The results from the tests are not gender differentiated, but we have been told that they can be and was done once in 1980 (S. Jernquist, Master thesis in pedagogy, 1982). (See Garmannslund, 1983)

There have been no research projects on mathematics and gender initiated by the authorities in Norway. There have been some single projects focusing on mathematics and gender, at the end of the 1970s and beginning of the 1980s. Jernquist (1982) did find some differences between girls and boys with respect to achievement in mathematics. Girls were not as good as boys at solving practically related problems but no other significant differences were found. Garmannslund (1983) commented on the difference saying that the practical problems had been taken mainly from the 'boys world'. But neither Jernquist nor Garmannslund made any comments on whether assessment style in itself can have any influence on gender differentiated achievements.

The results of the centralised examinations given at the end of grade 9 compulsory school, are not gender differentiated either. In 1978 an exception was made on a special request by Broch Utne and Haukaa (1980) to enable them to study gender differentiated performance. The results were sensational; they showed exactly the same tendency. In comparing the results from the examinations with the average marks based on classwork it showed that girls were *systematically* underestimated in relation to boys. Girls did score better at examinations than the marks given based on average classwork, and the opposite was the case for boys. Imsen (1980) conducted a larger survey in the lower secondary school. Both attitudes and grades were examined, and she did not find any significant gender differences in the mean marks given. Garmannslund's (1983) study focused much on attitudes and their impact on gender differentiated achievements, but not on styles of assessment with respect to their impact on gender differentiated achievement. Garmannslund's book created much debate when it was published in 1983 and the book is still often quoted. But in some way or another the great debate on gender and mathematics seemed to die with this book although why is not clear. Perhaps one explanation is that there has been a move away from looking for quantitative, concrete differences towards qualitative, abstract explanations. Nonetheless we find it paradoxical that, in the first decade under the Act on gender equality, gender and mathematics seem to be 'forgotten'. We have not been able to find answers, but a lot of questions arise connected to the issue.

Has the Act of Gender Equality become 'a pillow to sleep on'?

Has the focus been directed to discussion of decentralisation, centralisation and internationalisation?

Has the move in women's research from 'misery-research' to 'dignity-research' contributed to the lack of interest in girls' achievements in mathematics?

Has the general problem of raising money for research projects in school made it difficult to raise funds for projects defined as 'mathematics and gender'?

There exists only one article written recently (Brekke, 1990) where we can see a connection between the subject of mathematics and the general assessment debate. We will give a short summary of this article called: 'Testing av matematikkunnskapar — Kva er det?' ('Testing of Knowledge in Mathematics — What is that?') This article is part of the first EMIL report (Granheim, Lundgren and Tiller, 1990). The key-words in the article about mathematics are the same as those to be found in the final EMIL- report, (Granheim and Lundgren, 1990), and in the OECD-report: Competence, governance of qualities, assessment of results. The author mentions different styles of assessment from different countries: England, Wales, Scotland and the USA. A proposal is given for the Norwegian school system to introduce a test-system like the English APU (Assessment of Performance Unit) or the Scottish AAP (Assessment of Achievement Programme).

The author argues that work from a survey such as that found in the APU or AAP is important as a starting point for a discussion on quality because it throws light on the national profile from which quality will have to be discussed and assessed. (Brekke,1990 p. 343). But the author neither supplies any definition of national profile nor of quality. The author reflects on what competence in mathematics is supposed to be. This alone, we think, could be a point of departure for a discussion about mathematics in school, put into the context of competence since it is used as a keyword in current educational policy. The introduction of an official, national test system for mathematics into the Norwegian school system would break with the ideas of M87 where decentralised planning within each school and teaching adapted to the abilities of each pupil are important. Would not the inclusion of gender as part of a discussion of mathematics in school provide a broader, and more equitable, basis? The author does not mention the latter issue. There has, as far as we know, been no reaction to this article. We think that this indicates a lack of debate in Norway on the teaching of mathematics in the context of current educational policy.

It has now been decided that Norway is joining TIMSS, the Third International Mathematics and Science Study, prior participation having been restricted to the Second International Science Study. The question of testing, on international and national levels, has led to controversy among scientists and professionals concerned with the teaching of mathematics. Comment has already been made as to the lack of material connecting assessment to gender differentiated achievement in mathematics in the Norwegian school system. There exist no official statistics on marks given at the end of compulsory school. Although, in theory, it should be possible to get some gender differentiated information about marks in different subjects, including mathematics for pupils entering the upper secondary school, this seems to be a rather complicated process. In upper secondary school there exist official statistics on the results from every official examination. But unfortunately, these statistics are not differentiated according to gender. A quote from the 1987 OECD report underlines the dimensions of this problem:

> ... the examiners did not find it easy to comment on the use of educational resources, because data about them were almost completely absent. In examining international data we were surprised by the absence of material which could be useful to the Norwegian authorities for their own planning system.

As far as we know there exists no finished work on assessment, mathematics and gender from upper secondary school. Work by Sissel Gronmo (1990) focused upon the choice of mathematic courses in the upper secondary school. We turn, therefore, to a short summary of Liv Berge's ongoing research on Assessment, Mathematics and Gender for the degree of Master in Sociology at the University of Bergen. It includes material on gender differences in mathematics collected in upper secondary school. As a frame of reference we give a short description of the upper secondary school system, at national level. Almost all pupils (about 200,000) continue their education in upper secondary school. About 40% of these choose the area of General Study and the remaining 60% choose vocational high schools. (Astrup, 1991), (Appendix No.3)

Liv Berge's material is from the area of General Study. This area of study lasts for three years. The first year is compulsory, which means no streaming of the pupils. In the second year in upper secondary school, the pupils choose different subjects. After the first year, the pupils may continue without mathematics, or they can choose between two main courses 2MN (science mathematics) or 2MS (social science mathematics) The pupils may finish their education in mathematics after the second year, or continue in the last year of upper secondary school with 3MN or 3MS. The authorities set central examinations in all courses in mathematics in upper secondary school, in the area of General Study.

The research data has been collected from the compulsory course, 1MA, (5 periods/week), by questionnaire in 1990 (N=192) and 1991 (N=198), in two upper secondary schools, one in a rural area, one in an urban area. The material, which is only partly evaluated, shows strong evidence of a tendency for girls to abandon mathematics more frequently than boys in 2nd grade. Girls in rural areas quit most frequently. About 50% of the girls plan to continue with mathematics after 1st grade, compared to about 75% of the boys. This is about the same tendency as in the whole population of pupils. There has existed since 1986/87 gender differentiated material on the choices the pupils make in upper secondary school. These statistics show clearly that throughout the upper secondary school, boys are more likely to continue with mathematics than girls. And in addition girls seem to choose easier variants of the mathematics courses. (Appendix No.3)

Another tendency in the material shows that boys leaving lower secondary school have better marks entering upper secondary school than girls. In addition it shows clearly that girls' achievements in mathematics, measured in marks, drop between the 1st and 2nd term of the first year at upper secondary school. What do the pupils think about their marks? Do they consider them to be fair? The questionnaire included a question about the fairness of marks given both in lower secondary school and in upper secondary school. Girls and boys alike find the marks given in lower secondary school more just (about 80%) than the ones they receive in upper secondary school (about 60%). The material does not show any significant differences between the genders as to fairness in marks giving. This is a bit surprising in the context of the tendency that girls get lower marks during the school year. The material also indicates gender differences in looking at mathematics in connection to society. It also indicates gender differences in rural as compared with urban areas. As part of an extension of this work, it is planned to include analysis of the reasons given by the pupils for continuing or quitting mathematics. It is also proposed to interview a number of pupils.

Important further questions to ask:

- Are marks a good way to evaluate pupils' work?

- How do marks influence pupils' work?

- Do the examinations set by central authorities influence too greatly the process of learning and teaching?

- Do the central examinations leave little or no room for alternative work on mathematical problems?

- Has this style of assessment any impact on gender differentiated achievements?

- What should we use instead of centralised examinations and traditional marks to evaluate the work of the pupil?

- Why do we have such great differences between the genders?

- How do girls and boys consider mathematics in relationship to society, life and career?

- What are the consequences for the individuals and for society?

What kind of rationality is connected to mathematic as a school- subject? What kind of rationality is connected to use of tests, marks and centralised examinations? What kind of rationality is connected to girls and boys continuing or quitting mathematics? Can the different concepts of rationality developed by Norwegian women social scientists, technical limited rationality and responsible rationality (Ve, 1989), establish a framework to analyse the question of gender and mathematics in a sufficient way? To raise questions like these might bring gender issues in the teaching of mathematics into the current assessment debate.

However, as already stated, the official discussion on education focuses neither on styles of assessment nor work on new syllabuses. (RVO, 1987), (Astrup, 1991) Nor do the authorities take seriously that girls choose to quit mathematics. Statements like 'girls are now as good in mathematics as boys' appear relatively frequently, both orally and in publications. We have tried to investigate some of these statements, but they seem to be supported by few facts or built only on data too insubstantial for large-scale generalisations. We also have the impression that talking about girls' bad performance in general and in mathematics in particular is considered dangerous in case it is used to confirm the biological myth.

In a recent book (Haukaa, 1991), concluding the work of a large action programme for equality initiated by the government, we find the following:

> Today there are as many girls as boys in upper secondary school, and the science side is not dominated by the boys any more, since the girls take 41% of the places (1988-89). In addition to this there are as many girls as boys at universities and colleges, and the gender differences in the choice of university subjects are fading away.

This statement hides the fact that most of the girls doing science subjects are doing chemistry and biology. New statistical material from the universities shows that, as in the past, very few girls are doing mathematics at cand.scient and dr.scient level. Only about 7% of the scientific personnel at the mathematical institutes at universities are women. (Piene, 1988)

In spite of strong official work on gender equality, very few women in Norway influence the subject despite its centrality to and great impact on society.

Acknowledgements

The authors wish to thank all those in central government, in our school system and in various institutions who supplied information and opinions for this chapter. We also wish to thank friends and colleagues who assisted us so willingly.

References

Astrup, T. 1991: The present and future structure of education in mathematics in the Norwegian high school. RVO.

Brekke, G. 1990: Testing av matematikkunnskapar — Kva er det? I. Granheim, Lundgren og Tiller.

Brock-Utne, B. og Haukaa, R. 1980: Kunnskap uten makt. Universitetsforlaget.

Curriculum Guidelines for Compulsory Education in Norway 1987 (M87). English edition 1990, Aschehoug

Education in Norway 1990. Ministry of Education and Research. Oslo

Educational Statistics 1989. Upper secondary schools. Norges offisielle statistikk NOS B984

Garmannslund, K. 1983: Kan ikke jenter regne? Gyldendal Norsk Forlag

Granheim — Lundgren — Tiller 1990: Utdanningskvalitet — styrbar eller ustyrlig? Tano forlag

Granheim, M. og Lundgren U. 1990: Målstyring og evaluering i norsk skole. Sluttrapport fra EMIL-prosjektet. NORAS/LOS i utdanning

Grønnmo, L. S. 1991: Matematikk i videregående skole -et lykkelig valg? Hovudoppgave Universitetet i Oslo

Haukaa, R. (red) 1991: Nye kvinner — nye menn. Ad Notam. Oslo

Imsen, G 1981: Sokelys på matematikk i ungdomsskolen. Pedagogisk senter, Trondheim

Imsen, G. 1991: Effektivitet, motivasjon og kjonn. Om drivkrefter i pedagogisk arbeid. I (Monsen og Tiller)

Mellin-Olsen, S. (red) 1989: Om kunnskap — Fagdidaktiske perspektiver. Bergen Lærehogskole

Monsen,L. og Tiller,T (red) 1991: 'Effektive skoler' — skoleutvikling eller mer byråkrati? ad Notam Oslo

Monsterplan for Grunnskolen 1974 (M74), Aschehoug

OECD (1987): Reviews of National Policies for Education. Paris 1990

OECD 1987: Reviews of National Policies for Education. Norway. Report to OECD. Oslo

Piene, R. (1988): Jenter og matematikk. Skriftserie nr.8 fra Senter for realfagsundervisning.

Raaen, F. D. 1990: Elevvurdering i nytt perspektiv. Sluttrapport for prosjektet:'Vurdering og veiledning' Grunnskolerådet.

Report No.37 to Storting (1990-91) Concerning organisation and management in education sector. (Summary)

RVO (1987): Reform av videregående skolematematikk. Innstilling fra en arbeidsgruppe.

RVO (1988): Skolevurdering. Eit grunnlagsdokument.

RVO (1990): Seks skoler — seks verdener. RVOs skolevurderingsprosjekt. Oppsummering og refleksjoner etter forste års arbeid. Av T.Tiller

RVO (1990): Kvalitetsstyring og kvalitetssikring i skolen. Idegrunnlag og gjennomforing. Av I.Bjorndal

RVO (1991): Bjorndal — Tiller — Simons: National Aims and Local Freedom. The National Council for Upper Secondary Education, Norway 1991.

Solvang, R. 1986: Matematikkdidaktikk. NKI-forlaget

St.meld. nr.33 (1991-92): Kunnskap og kyndighet. Om visse sider ved videregående opplæring.

St.meld. nr.37 (1990-91): Om organisering og styring i utdanningssektoren.

Telhaug, A. O. 1979: Vår nye videregående skole. 3.utg. Didakta norsk forlag. Oslo.

Tiller, T. 1990: Kenguruskolen — det store spranget. Gyldendal Norsk Forlag A/s

Ve, H. og Fjelde, N. (1991): Public private tendencies within higher education in Norway from a women's perspective. Kelly, G. P. and Slaughter S. (eds) Women's Higher Education in Comparative Perspective

Ve, H. 1989: Educational planning and rational ambiguity. Paper presented at the VIIth World Congress of Comparative Education. Canada.

APPENDIX 1: The Education System

Organization and structure

In the Norwegian education system the Storting has the legislative and levying power. The Government exerts its authority in matters of education through the ministries. Since 1982 there have been two ministries for education, viz:

— **Ministry of Church and Education**: Primary and secondary education (7 to 19) and adult education.

— **Ministry of Cultural and Scientific Affairs**: Higher Education (including teacher training) and research.

Pre-school education is under the authority of the Ministry of Consumer Affairs, cf. above.

Norwegion education system (Typical paths).

The two ministries dealing with education act upon the professional advice of various national councils and bodies. At present there are councils for the various types of education and training, including a Sami Education Council giving advice concerning educational provisions and curricula for the Sami population. Due to the many national councils and ad-hoc bodies in the school sector the relationship between the Ministry of Church and Education and the advisory councils/bodies is being revised. The revision might lead to a reorganisation of the administrative structure at central level.

The responsibility for the running of the primary and lower secondary schools rests with the municipalities, while the counties are responsible for upper secondary education. In higher education the administrative responsibility has to a great extent been delegated to the individual universities and institutions.

(Education in Norway, 1990)

APPENDIX 2: Allocation of teaching periods in the compulsory school (M87):

	Primary stage			Lower sec. stg.
	Grades 1.-3.	Grades 4.-6.	Sum gr. 1.-6.	Grades 7.-9.
Religious Instruction	6	6	12	6
Norwegian	17	16	33	14
Mathematics	11	11	22	11 [1]
English		7	7	9
Civics	6	15	21	
Social Studies				9
Natural Science				8
Music	3	6	9	3
Arts and Crafts	4	12	16	5
Physical Education	4	6	10	8
Home Economics		3	3	4
Optional subjects				11
Pupil/class council	30*	60*	90*	2
Practical, social and cultural work	50*	75*	125*	150*
Sum	51	82	133	90
At local disposal			5	
Total			138	90

*Total minimum number of periods/total number or teaching periods during a three-year block. These activities are integrated into all subjects.

1) The Municipal Education Committee is free to allocate more lessons a week than the minimum number of lessons. This is done in different municipalities. Minimum weekly lessons in mathematics can be allocated like this:

grades:	weekly lessons:	assessment:[2]
9.	4	
8.	3	marks are given for compulsory
7.	4.	subjects twice a year
6.	4	
5.	4	
4.	3	no formal assessment
3.	4	
2.	4	
1.	3	

2) Assessment and evaluation.
The revised curriculum Guidelines propose varied forms of assessment at all levels. Emphasis is put on forms of assessment which are suitable for providing guidance to pupils and stimulating the learning process. It is laid down that parents and guardians must be informed of their child's progress at least twice a year, either through personal meeting or by means of written reports. There is no formal assessment during the six years of primary school. At the lower secondary stage pupils are given marks for compulsory subjects twice a year, and there is a final written examination organised by the Council for Primary and Lower Secondary Education. (Education in Norway, 1990)

APPENDIX 3

Courses in mathematics in upper secondary school:

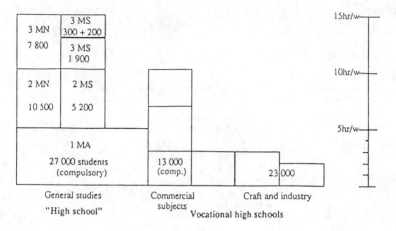

(Astrup, 1991)

MATHEMATICS IN UPPER SECONDARY SCHOOL, GENERAL STUDIES.

1990/91	3MN: 8331		3MS: 1580			
	GIRLS 2896	BOYS 5435	GIRLS 763	BOYS 817		
1989/90	2MN: 10489		2MS: 5230		QUIT: 11912	
	GIRLS 4291	BOYS 6198	GIRLS 2693	BOYS 2537	GIRLS 7150	BOYS 2794
1988/89	1MA: (COMPULSORY) 25663					
	GIRLS 14134	BOYS 11529				

CHAPTER NINE

Portugal

Joao Filipe Matos
Leonor Cunha Leal

Introduction

After the approval of the comprehensive law on the educational system in 1986, a process of reform started in Portugal. One of the aspects of this reform deals with the system of assessment of students' achievements stated by a new law. In order to place the present situation in context, this chapter presents a brief history of the educational system and its main features. The new system of assessment is discussed from the perspective of teachers as well as our own views. Finally, present concerns about assessment in mathematics education are set in the context of the Portuguese new curricula, with preliminary questions on differential performance.

According to the comprehensive law on the educational system

> education furthers the development of democratic and pluralist ideas which embody respect for others and their ideas and is open to dialogue and free exchange of opinions, forming citizens able constructively to criticise their social system and capable of working towards its progressive transformation (GEP, 1987, p.8).

Basic education is universal, compulsory and free and lasts for nine years[1]. However, compulsory attendance of basic education ends at 15 years of age. The objectives of basic education emphasise the guarantee to all citizens of a general education which ensures they discover and develop their interests and aptitudes, ability and reason, memory and spirit of enquiry, creativity and sense of moral and aesthetic awareness, promoting individual fulfilment in harmony with values of social solidarity.

In Portugal, most of the schools are public. The Ministry of Education organises centrally all issues concerning school management, curriculum development and evaluation, having control over teacher appointments. The guide lines are defined by a central department of the Ministry. Five regional authorities execute the global orientations of the Ministry and deal with specific school-related issues in each region.

In 1986, just after the approval of the comprehensive laws on the educational system, a process of reform began. This reform, led by the Ministry of Education, is intended to be both comprehensive and global. It includes the creation of new professional schools, the reorganisation of the set of school disciplines and the development of new curricula, the establishment of a new system of administration for schools and the design of a new assessment system.

With respect to curricula, the main features of the reform deal with a slightly different structure. There are two phases: basic education, with three levels[2] (the first level going from grade 1 to 4, 6-10 years old, the 2nd level including the 5th and 6th grades, 10-12 years, and the 3rd level going from 7th to 9th grade, 12-15 years). Secondary education, from 10th to 12th grade (15-18 years), was also re-structured. The different areas of study have a broader dimension and try to form 'scenarios' for students to choose their vocational disciplines (see Figure 1 below) in a more appropriate way.

In 10th grade, students may choose one of two branches: (a) the technical-professional branch, which allows them to enter the workforce after three years, and (b) the studies that give access to the university.

A new dimension of curriculum activity is called 'school area'. The idea is to have different disciplines giving a part of their time to involving students in interdisciplinary activities and projects which are expected to increase their ability to bring together different areas of knowledge.

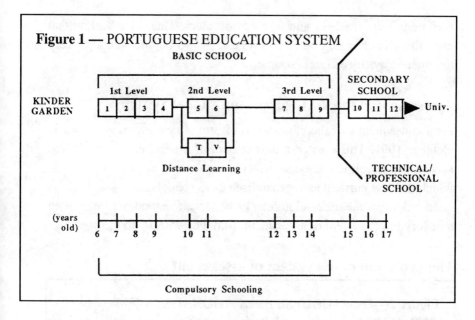

Figure 1 — PORTUGUESE EDUCATION SYSTEM

Since the approval of the comprehensive law on the educational system, laws have been published setting the framework for the intended changes. Different departments of the Ministry are in charge of laying out the plans concerning the several aspects of the reform and for the actual implementation. In most cases, the drafts of the laws and regulations are submitted for discussion by teachers, teacher educators, parents' associations and teachers' unions. In relation to specific aspects of the different curricula, the Ministry directly asks invited teachers to express their opinions and suggestions. The final decisions are always made by the Ministry and in some cases against the majority of expressed opinions. This process can be viewed as a classic 'top down' approach to educational reform. In fact, the major addressees, teachers and students, have little or no significant input into the development process of the reform.

Since 1990, the reform has been implemented in phases. In 1991/92 the 1st grade was generalised to all schools. In the school year of 1990/91 an experiment was conducted with the curricula of 5th, 7th and 10th grade in a number of schools. In 1991/92 these same schools are experimenting with the curricula for grades 6, 8 and 11. Next year the curriculum reform will be generalised to all schools in 5th and 7th grade.

Neither the new administrative nor the assessment arrangements have yet been implemented. But they are being discussed in seminars and conferences by teachers and teacher educators. There is a feeling that everything is changing but the change seems to be understood in very divergent ways by different people.

Assessment in the Portuguese Educational System

As a consequence of the educational reform, a new law was passed in October 1991. This created a new system of assessment for basic and secondary schools to come into effect in each grade, in the school year in which the new curricula are generalised to all schools.

In order that the innovations can be better understood, we begin with a history of the system of assessment from the 1950s up to the present.

The evolution of the system of assessment

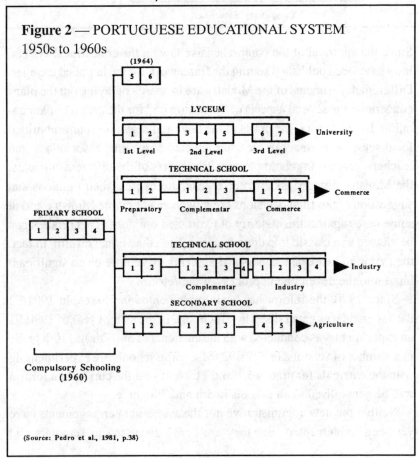

Figure 2 — PORTUGUESE EDUCATIONAL SYSTEM
1950s to 1960s

(Source: Pedro et al., 1981, p.38)

202

From 1950s to 1960s

As we can see in figure 2 above, the Portuguese educational system began with a level of four years of primary school, followed by a choice between Lyceum, Technical School, subdivided in two areas according to the professional area (commerce or industry) and Secondary School.

The first three years of primary school were meant to give the basis of education, its main content being spelling, writing and counting. The fourth year was complementary providing essential knowledge for those who would not proceed with their studies. Classifications were expressed in a qualitative way, and were allocated using the following: 'Bad', 'Inferior', 'Sufficient', 'Good', or 'Very Good'. At the end of each year, there was the possibility of a student repeating a class. At the end of this phase, those students who wished to continue their studies and enter the Lyceum would have to do a set of tests, called 'the Lyceum entrance examination'. This examination would give a certificate similar to the one they achieved at the end of the fourth grade.

These national examinations had the same basic items and consisted of written and oral tests. The written test included mathematics, drawing and Portuguese (with a dictation, a composition and a comprehension). The oral examination focused on Portuguese, mathematics, history, geography and natural sciences. These last three subjects had, in a prior period, been included in the written test. The results of these examinations were given as 'approved' or 'not approved'. If a number of conditions, such as fewer than a stipulated number of spelling errors or errors in a set of mathematical problems, were not met, a pupil could fail right there in the written test.

In 1952, concern with the three years of compulsory schooling was expressed leading to a new law (in 1956) which specified that primary school would be compulsory for all male students until the end of the fourth year.

From Figure 2 we can see that since 1964 two more years were added to primary education (the 'complementary level') for those who did not want to go on studying. This was the result of the demand for qualified workers and the economic development needs of the country. These two years were mandatory for those children who enrolled in the 1st grade in 1964/65.

The Lyceum was divided into three levels. The first (two years) had five disciplines that were the object of assessment (the scores determining if the student succeeded or failed). These were Portuguese, French, geography, natural sciences, mathematics and drawing. Some other disciplines (music, gymnastics, religion and handiwork) completed the curriculum but were not objects of assessment.

The assessment made during these two years had a very strong scoring nature, its function being essentially classification and selection. The scores defined by the teachers at the end of each term were based on the results of tests, and were expressed in a 0-20 scale. The students who had a score under 4 were excluded and could not proceed with their studies in that year. To pass from the first to the second year of Lyceum it was necessary to obtain, in each discipline, 29 points as the sum of the scores over the three terms. At the end of the first level the student had another examination which was a national test with a written and an oral part. Students would be approved if they got at least 9.5 points (in a 0-20 scale) in four disciplines, as long as the final average was not below 9.5 points. Otherwise they would have to repeat all the disciplines of the second year.

The second level of the Lyceum was divided into two sections, humanities (four disciplines) and science (five disciplines). The conditions for the progression of studies were identical to those referred to above. The concept of assessment was the same, based on the same kind of tests. At the end of the second level of study, there was also a national examination. As in the previous case, in each discipline the students were approved if they had a minimum score of 9.5 points. Scores under 9.5 in two disciplines of the same section led to repetition of all the disciplines of that section. If the students failed in two disciplines, one from each section, they could choose which section they would repeat.

The objectives of the third level were clearly oriented to the preparation of the students who would enter the university. This level was over two years and was divided into different areas. In each area the disciplines were independent from each other in terms of progression from the first to the second year and also in terms of final examination. This examination was again a nation-wide written test.

From 1960s to 1970s

In 1967 the Ministry of Education took the first step towards the unification of the different types of school in Portugal. In order to postpone students' choice, it was decided to unify the first level of the Lyceum with the 'preparatory level of the technical school' creating the 'preparatory level of secondary school' (see Figure 3).

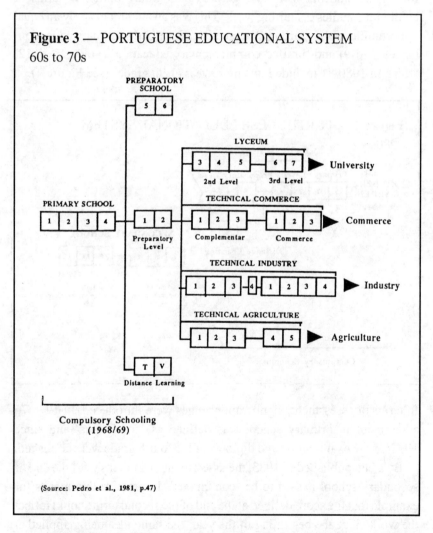

Figure 3 — PORTUGUESE EDUCATIONAL SYSTEM
60s to 70s

(Source: Pedro et al., 1981, p.47)

In 1968 the same law that defined the preparatory level abolished the national admission examination to Lyceum.

From 1970s to 1980s

Since the beginning of the 1970s and with a new law of comprehensive education, some effort was made to develop compulsory schooling. After the revolution of 1974 deep changes transformed the whole country. Democracy brought new influences to the educational system. The democratisation of the educational structures imposed a new common strand for all the students with no regard to their future option in terms of continuing studies or starting work. This was an attempt to apply an equal opportunities policy through the creation of 'unified secondary education' (grade 7 to 9) and 'unified complementary education' (grade 10 to 12) which in 1980/81 included one more year (12th grade) (see Figure 4).

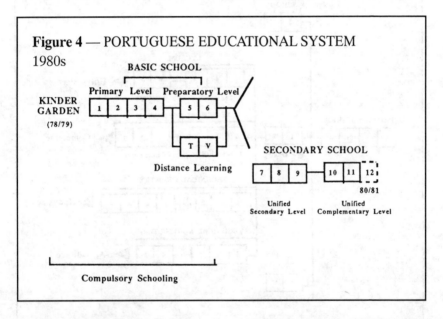

Figure 4 — PORTUGUESE EDUCATIONAL SYSTEM

In terms of assessment, significant changes were introduced. In 1975/76 assessment in primary school was defined as 'continuous' and since 1977/78 the examination and diploma of the fourth grade were abolished.

By a law published in 1983, the assessment of students until the end of secondary school is said to be 'continuous'. In practice this means for example that the score defined at the end of the second term should reflect the work since the beginning of the year, the same idea being applied at the end of the third term. In primary school the assessment is descriptive. From 5th to 9th grade the final assessment is associated with a score (on a 1-5 scale). In the 'unified complementary' the score is maintained on a 0-20 scale.

In 1983, and after a phase in which the final examinations were the responsibility of each school, they were abolished. New conditions were defined for the students to go from a given grade to the next one; for example, from 5th to 9th grade, more than two scores below 3 (in a 1-5 scale) dictates repetition of the grade.

Finally, at the end of the 12th grade the students who wanted to enter university sat a final examination.

The present educational system

As already mentioned, a new comprehensive law on the educational system was passed in 1986. In 1988, progression of students through the first level (1st to 4th grade) changed. Two 'phases', the first including the 1st and 2nd grades and the second, the 3rd to 4th grades, were established and repetition of grade was only considered at the end of each phase. A previous law had stated that assessment of the students would be mainly formative, continuous and the responsibility of the teacher.

In summary, Figures 5, 6 and 7 show the evolution of the compulsory school and the assessment system in Portugal.

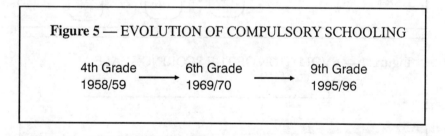

Figure 5 — EVOLUTION OF COMPULSORY SCHOOLING

4th Grade	6th Grade	9th Grade
1958/59	1969/70	1995/96

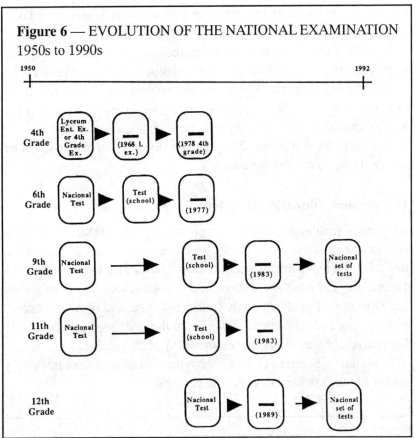

Figure 6 — EVOLUTION OF THE NATIONAL EXAMINATION 1950s to 1990s

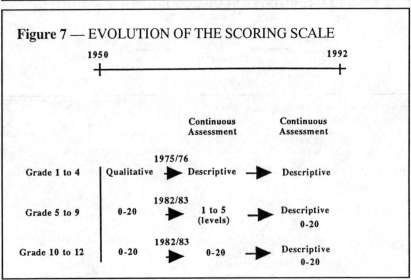

Figure 7 — EVOLUTION OF THE SCORING SCALE

The new system of assessment

Any process of reform necessarily demands a system of assessment aligned with the principles and goals of the educational system. This is the situation currently evolving in Portugal.

The antecedent of the law

In 1990 the Ministry of Education distributed a draft of a document on the new system of assessment. It was to be discussed by the teachers, and each group of teachers at the school would provide feedback. For this purpose the Ministry prepared a questionnaire (IIE, 1991a). One of the main innovations was the attempt to make repetition of class across each level of the compulsory school more difficult. The results of this inquiry showed that (a) 61% of the teachers did not agree with summative assessment taking place only at the end of each level of study, (b) half of the teachers were against the *exceptional nature* of the so-called 'exceptional summative assessment', and (c) 43% of them were against the exceptional nature of repetition of class. Even the consideration of the different coefficients for the calculation of the average at the end of the basic school had 40% of teachers against. From these results, it seemed that teachers were unwilling to accept barriers to their control of students' repetition of class. As the process of class repetition has a long tradition in Portugal, is it the case that teachers are afraid to lose control of it? The opinions of the unions and associations of teachers were also considered and analysed (IIE, 1991b).

Unlike previous occasions, the discussion of this document was widespread and not only amongst those involved in education. Articles and editorials were published in newspapers, both criticising and supporting the proposal for the new system of assessment. For example, the association of teachers of mathematics approved a position paper criticising the new system of assessment, in particular concerning the creation of 'classes of students in introductory level' instead of differentiated groups and the reintroduction of the 0-20 scale. This paper was published in the magazine *Educaçao e Matemática* and it was submitted to a department of the Ministry of Education (APM, 1990).

Finally, in October, 1991, a law on the system of assessment was passed. It was similar to the proposal, with minor improvements with respect to its formulation and accuracy about certification. However, debates about this issue have continued. After the official approval of the law the Ministry organised a seminar in March 1992 which aimed 'to identify problems arising from the application of the new system of assessment and to make recommendations and suggestions for its improvement in the future'. Teachers from universities and schools of education were invited to participate. One of the authors of this chapter who was present, noted that, from 13 plenary presentations focusing on the system of assessment, only one clearly supported the options in the law. All the others displayed disagreement as well as pointing to difficulties in the implementation of the law.

Meanwhile, the Minister of Education changed and in June 1992 a new law replaced the former one. This established a new system of assessment for the compulsory school, maintaining what had been in existence at the secondary level.

New aspects of the law

The law states clearly that the school is directly 'responsible for the schooling course of the students and must guarantee the achievement of the objectives of compulsory schooling and the educational success of the students'. The assessment of the students in compulsory school is based on the input of the team of teachers involved, on the participation of the students themselves and on their parents. Four categories of assessment are considered: formative, summative, 'gauged' and specialised.

Formative assessment is 'the main way to assess the curriculum structure of the basic school'. It is intended to inform students, teachers and parents about the quality of the learning and teaching process, to determine the degree of achievement of curriculum objectives, and to support decisions about the need for methodological adaptations, learning support or curricular changes when difficulties are identified. This kind of assessment must be based on data from knowledge and skills, capacities and attitudes developed by the students. Although it has a 'systematic and continued character', formal moments exist at the end of each term, in the 2nd and 3rd level, to express a descriptive and qualitative evaluation.

Summative assessment 'takes into account the quality of the teaching and learning process', resulting in a global judgement about the development of the students' knowledge and skills, capacities and attitudes. The objective is now to decide if the student must repeat or pass, after having tried all the educational resources and supports. Taking place usually at the end of each term, it is expressed in a 1-5 scale, followed by a summary of the descriptive results of the formative assessment for the 2nd and 3rd level, and in a descriptive way on the 1st level. At the end of each level it is expressed by the categories 'approved' or 'not approved'.

The gauged assessment is aimed (a) 'to assess the degree of achievement of curriculum objectives' for each level of the compulsory schooling and (b) to assess 'the educational system at a national, regional and local dimension'. The first one can occur at the beginning of the 2nd and 3rd level, and is the responsibility of the schools. The second one can occur any time and has no implications for the students. The Ministry has the responsibility for its development.

Finally, specialised assessment is the responsibility of the supervision and counselling services. This kind of assessment can only be required by the teacher in the case of the first level or by the 'pedagogical council' of the school after a proposal from the group of teachers of a given class.

In order to respond to non-satisfactory results, 'programs or action plans' are considered which include both content and pedagogical processes. The activities can have a disciplinary, an interdisciplinary or a transdisciplinary nature. They must be guaranteed by the school when teachers identify learning difficulties and are meant to enable the accomplishment of curricula objectives. Teachers directly responsible for them must write a report, at the end of each term, which includes their opinion about the maintenance or abandonment of these procedures.

The decision that a student must repeat a grade always has 'an exceptional character' and it is only accepted after the above actions have been shown not to work. Failure results if 'the summative assessment reveals too great a distance between the curriculum objectives and a student's capacities defined at the national and local level'.

By the end of the 3rd level a diploma certificate is given to the students who have been approved in the summative assessment. The students who have not achieved at this level and have already reached the age limit for compulsory schooling can ask for a 'certificate of frequency' of the basic school. However, later, if they want to gain their diploma they must take an exam, and the school must give them all possible support.

Critical aspects of the law

We believe that the new system of assessment for the compulsory school brings positive changes compared with the previous reform. From our point of view, positively and critically, the more relevant aspects of this law are:

1. There is a recognition of a global concern, different from the past, to include the students and their parents in the assessment process. This is a step forward, although at the outset some difficulties may occur around the definition of the conditions of participation.

2. A need for the school's responsibility for equality of opportunity to educational access and success to be clarified has been recognised.

3. A students' portfolio that follows them through their basic education has been introduced. It includes all relevant developmental information and is confidential.

4. Making the repetition of classes an exception in compulsory school is, we believe, a positive change. From results in different countries, it is clear that repeating a class does not alter the likelihood of a student's success. On the contrary, it increases the disadvantage and the mal-adaptation both in the school and society. As school will be compulsory until the end of the basics (9th grade) and repeating will be a more expensive solution for the educational system (and less acceptable in pedagogical terms), a reduction in its use is not only acceptable but even desired.

5. Several different methods of implementing repetition of classes are being introduced: the student may have to repeat all subjects or a supportive plan, specific to that student, may integrate only certain subjects or areas of studies.

6. The existence of a gauged assessment of the educational system at national, regional and local level does not interfere in the student's school progress.

7. From our point of view, the idea that emerges from the law is that formative assessment is an instrument to regulate the work of teacher and student. Its objective is to inform the student, the parents and the teacher about the accomplishment of curriculum objectives in order to establish new objectives, correct errors and malfunctions, choose

new methods and search for alternative resources. Summative assessment decides the progress or retention of the student in a given level and the kind of certificate that the student deserves. From that perspective, it is unclear why a summative assessment is considered necessary at the end of each term and at the end of the intermediate grade. Even for those students who are not able to achieve the curriculum's objectives, despite the provision of support procedures, summative assessment does not provide a solution.

8. The existence of both formative and summative assessments at the same moment is also critical. How can one be sure that the procedures that emerge from the formative assessment have failed or will fail?

We believe that this law is an answer to pedagogical questions raised in the different debates that have accompanied the process of creating a new assessment system. However, its implementation demands a number of conditions including teacher training to ensure the implementation of the spirit of this law.

Assessment in Mathematics Education: Some Current Issues

The reform in mathematics education

The new curriculum for secondary school mathematics is organised in three strands: knowledge, abilities and attitudes/values. According to those responsible in the Ministry, one of the major aims of the new curricula was to improve students' attitudes towards mathematics. The process of learning must be centred on the student, who is expected to become an active participant. More intuitive approaches to mathematical concepts, with emphasis on graphical representations and concrete situations, are some of the new orientations. Other features of the new curriculum include the introduction of probability and statistics at an earlier level and greater attention to geometry. From the 10th grade, calculus is still the main subject. In terms of teaching methodologies, the use of calculators has been recommended from grade 5 and group work is supported. In grades 7 to 9, problem solving is said to be the mainstream of the curricula. From 5th to 12th grade students have four mathematics classes per week, each one of 50 minutes.

As a part of this educational reform, an experiment in the implementation of a new mathematics curriculum for 7th and 10th grades, and a new 10th grade discipline called Quantitative Methods, was conducted in a number of selected schools during the school year of 1990/91. At the request of a department of the Ministry of Education which is in charge of the evaluation of the whole process of reform, some studies, using different research designs, were carried out by different research teams from several universities (see for example Ponte et al., 1991). Aiming to identify the major problems associated with the implementation of the reform in mathematics education, the results of these studies are beginning to reach mathematics educators and discussion becomes more reflective.

Discussion of assessment as a result of the implementation of the new mathematics curricula

As has already been noted, one of the innovations of the new mathematics curriculum is that it is organised in three strands: knowledge, abilities and attitudes/values. For the first time, the last mentioned strand appears as important, addressing, as it does, the improvement of students' attitudes towards mathematics. Despite the fact that it was well accepted by mathematics teachers, it created a new difficulty for them. How can attitudes be assessed? What are adequate forms and instruments for this purpose?

Although the mention of abilities and skills is not new in the curricula, it is true that nowadays their relevance is growing. More and more the role of problem solving, the ability to use mathematical language to communicate ideas, to analyse situations, to investigate and generalise, become important in mathematics education. Once again this situation generates difficulty for the teachers. How can teachers assess students' thinking processes and strategies and students' learning potential? How can higher order thinking be assessed in mathematics?

Furthermore, rejecting a passive role for students, the learning process is considered in the curriculum as essentially a construction (and not an absorption). This construction should appear naturally in appropriate contexts. Diversity of experiences should be offered to students through a variety of ways of learning, using calculators (computers are accepted), manipulative materials, real world situations as well as theoretical ones. To be compatible with these new ways of facing the process of learning, new forms and instruments of assessment are necessary. But which ones are suitable? How to do it? How to score them?

New mathematics curricula suggest different methods to be used in the process of teaching. Contrary to the traditional situation in Portuguese classes, group work is also considered as an important method. Mathematics teachers however are only trained to assess individual work.

Assessment in mathematics education: an increasing problem

Difficult questions and serious problems with respect to assessment in mathematics education are not new. But nowadays, because of the Portuguese situation of reform, teachers are facing new challenges. For example, for the first time at the annual congress of the Portuguese Association of Teachers of Mathematics (APM), assessment in mathematics education was the theme for a discussion group and for a panel. Assessment was also identified as one of the areas considered to be more difficult by those teachers who participated in the experiments with the new mathematics curricula in 1990/91. APM organised a seminar in May 1991, with a number of invited participants from universities, schools of education and secondary and elementary schools. We will focus on the outcomes of this event.

The seminar took place over two days. On the second day, the participants worked in small groups reflecting upon one of the following topics: (a) assessment and problem solving, or (b) assessment methods and instruments. The final products of this work were several recommendations concerning each of these topics.

1. Assessment and problem solving:

- Although the focus should be on the process used in problem solving activities, we can only assess students' products. It is important to establish a difference between answer and resolution.

- Students' work on problem solving can be developed in different ways — writing, oral, and technology based.

- When assessing problem solving activities in group work there are reasons to distinguish between the assessment of the group's work and the assessment of the individual's participation. The first one focuses on the work, viewed in general as the product of the group and not the sum of the contributions of the different members. The second one is based on an individual process beyond the product.

- When activities such as project work are being assessed, it is important to emphasise a global assessment of the products of the work and its evolution, instead of a separated assessment based on a certain number of pre-established criteria.

- The student's work or the group's work should be assessed in an holistic way.

- To assess problem solving activities it is useful for the teacher to have records such as written documents produced by the students, work sheets of problems solved in regular lessons and notes concerning the observation of oral performance.

- Teachers should organise a personal record of each student which could be used whenever they want. This process is naturally flexible according to the circumstances and teachers' style of work.

- Assessment of problem solving is a difficult task. Efforts must be made to include multiple sources of information, not forgetting that the investment in problem solving should be an important factor of development instead of one more factor of frustration and an instrument of selection.

2. Assessment methods and instruments:

- There is a need for a balance between the *scoring assessment* and the *regulation assessment*, giving more weight to the implementation of the former.

- Decisions concerning assessment of students' achievement should be made on the basis of a convergence of information obtained from a variety of sources, including different work styles, such as individual, group or whole class, different duration and type of activities (oral, written, manipulative and technology based).

- The need for a variety of sources of information is also applied to written products. Teachers should consider written reports and texts as important as traditional tests.

- Tests should show variety in style and mode of application. For example, short tests with only one or two questions, tests with open-ended questions, with or without consulting texts or note-books, and two-stage tests.

- If new indicators of the learning process not pre-established appear during the development of the work, they should also be taken into consideration by the teacher.

Differential performance in Mathematics

Among the 68 million students of the EC girls represent about 49% (Commission des Comunitées Européennes, 1990). But after the age of 15 years in most countries, boys are overrepresented in education[3] which implies that more girls than boys tend to leave at the end of compulsory schooling. In this matter, Portugal is a remarkable exception: for all ages, there are more girls than boys in school.

However, data does not exist to indicate if Portuguese girls perform better or worse than boys in mathematics. In the preparation of this chapter we tried to have access to data from the Ministry of Education that could help us to show a picture of Portuguese students' achievement in mathematics. However the lack of organised information in the Ministry of Education means that it is impossible to make judgements with respect to students' achievement in mathematics even at the end of the 6th and 9th grades.[4]

We did, however, have access to data from two schools. The first is a junior high school in Lisbon, with 1600 students from 5th to 9th grade (most of them with a high socio-economic background) and 153 teachers (75% of them having a professional degrees). Data from this school show that, in 6th grade, half of the students are girls but they represent 57% of the students that did not succeed in mathematics. We can also note that 27% of boys and 37% of girls failed. In a second school, out of the capital, with 4500 students from 7th to 12th grade (with low socio-economic background), and 270 teachers (about 60% with professional degrees), the situation is quite different. In 9th grade (41% girls), about 40% of the students who failed are girls, 40% of the girls, 50% of the boys did not succeed.

We do not know how this data matches the global situation in Portugal. We believe that the situation is very complex and differences would be found between different regions of the country. Data is needed to investigate differential performance in mathematics. However we would say that by the end of compulsory school (9th grade) all students have few resources with which to face failure and we do not believe that the new system of assessment just approved will help in this.

Students' achievement is under-represented in research on mathematics education in Portugal. We believe that more research is needed to promote a broader discussion of this issue in the context of the reform of the educational system. The lack of data with respect to students' progress implies that the educational authorities and educators are not sensitive to problems of evaluation and assessment, and their differential implications.

Notes

1. This objective will be fulfilled by the students who complete the 9th grade in 1995/96 until when compulsory schooling ends with the 6th grade.
2. Level stands for a number of years of study which correspond to a unit with a specific curriculum.
3. The present volume does not bear this out. (Editor's note)
4. The 6th grade is currently the last year of compulsory schooling, soon to be extended to the 9th grade.

References

Associaçao de Professores de Mathemática (1990). *Avaliaçao: uma questao a enfrentar. Actas do seminário sobre avaliaçao*, Lisboa: APM.

Commission des Communautés Européennes (1990). *Les Filles et les Garçons dans l'Enseignement secondaire et Superieur*, Bruxelles.

GEP, Gabinete de Estudos e Planeamento (1987). *Comprehensive Law on the Educational System*, Law 46/86, Portugal, Lisboa: GEP.

IIE, Instituto de Inovaçao Educacional (1991a). *Opiniao dos professores dos ensinos Básico e Secundário relativamente ás medidas constantes no projecto do Sistema de Avaliaçao dos alunos*, Lisboa: IIE.

IIE, Instituto de Inovaçao Educacional (1991b). *Análise de Pareceres de Associaçoes e Institutçooes de Educaçao sobre o projecto do Sistema de Avaliaçao dos alunos*. Lisboa: IIE.

Pedro, E., Leal, L., Colliander, M., Costa, M., Coutinho, L., Hanglund, S. e Lundgren, U. (1981). *Avaliaçao do ensino secundário unificado. A caminho duma reforma do ensino secundário unificado*. Lisboa: GEP.

Ponte, J., Matos, J., Guimaraes, H., Leal, L. & Canavarro, A. (1991). *Experimenting new curricula*. (Paper submitted for publication in Educational Studies and Mathematics.

CHAPTER TEN

Spain

María Jesús Luelmo
María Eugenia Jiménez
Fidela Velázquez

The Most Important Changes in the Spanish Education System

Experimental programmes and didactic innovations

Since the end of the 1970s, with the new growth of democratic development and open conditions in the country the inadequacy of the education system was openly recognised in Spanish society. Prior to this, an academic secondary schooling was completely separated from practical applications; it was encyclopaedic and not adjusted to the possibilities of the school syllabus. In the case of mathematics, it was heavily influenced by modern mathematics. These factors, among others, resulted in the symptoms of what is known as 'schooling failure'.

In response, in 1983, the Education Ministry began an experimental reform of secondary schooling (14-18 years) in an annually increasing number of schools. This experimental reform focused on syllabus and pedagogic change and also encouraged the development of modules for vocational education at level three in line with the instructions of the EC.

In 1984, the experimental reform of the compulsory school started (12-14 years).

Also at this time, Teachers' Centres were established to support and spread the work which formerly had been sited in universities and private institutions. Pedagogic renovation movements have a long tradition in Spain. In the late 70s, Mathematical Associations were formed. Through their bulletins, meetings and seminars, innovative methods were publicised. The combination of the availability of information on teaching methods and the need to implement new schooling demands, encouraged more teachers to work in groups and to design and develop innovative projects in their classrooms, sometimes with the support of the educational administrations.

The need for a structural reform

The evaluation of the experimental reforms of secondary and compulsory schooling, although a positive experience in curricular innovation especially in mathematics, showed clearly the need for making deeper changes. There were also political reasons which advised these changes such as the imminent entrance of Spain into the EC and the decentralisation of responsibilities about educational matters from the government to local educational authorities. It may be important to explain this.

At present action about education matters is the responsibility of the Education Ministry. This is a Constitutional guarantee that the needs of all students are met, in line with a national policy to ensure a certain homogeneity from different educational experiences. However local educational administrations in the autonomous regions (Andalucía, Canarias, Galicia, País Vasco, Cataluña, Valencia and Navarra), are responsible for the implementation of policy directives, with the Education Ministry being responsible for other regions of Spain. It is hoped that this decentralisation process in education will be complete in 4 or 5 years time. So, the new Reform has to start in a more open and general way which allows its adaptation and interpretation in each autonomous region.

General lines in the Reform

In 1988, a public debate was opened with respect to structural aspects of the reform. The most interesting points are:

- Compulsory schooling will end at sixteen instead of fourteen years as at present.

- Compulsory schooling will be divided into two phases (6-12) and Secondary (12-16). This compares with the current arrangement for compulsory schooling called *Enseñanza General Básica* (Basic General Education) (6-14) and non-compulsory schooling: *Bachillerato* (Academic education) (14-18), or *Formación profesional* (Vocational education) (14-19).

- Compulsory secondary education will be common to all students, with certain diversification in the final year (see Figure 1, page 224).

In the course of the school year 1989-90, when the general proposal had been widely accepted the Education Ministry presented for debate a 'Basic Curriculum Design', which is a detailed document with educational objectives for each phase of different curriculum subjects.

The results of this public debate of the new curriculum, the report made by experts and the political and technical negotiations between the Education Ministry, have finally led to the establishment of national 'Minimum Teaching' (July, 1991), which has to serve as the basis for the future regionally autonomous curricula. The intention is that teachers should take the ultimate decisions in the curricular process of the core curriculum, adapting programmes and materials in to adjust to students' needs.

The reform began in 1992-93 in the first primary classes (6-8 years), and will continue step by step. Several pilot experiments have begun in a few schools, nearly all of them from experimental schools which participated in the last reform. Some of the autonomous communities have been implementing it for several years. Also, the development of vocational education modules at Levels 2 and 3 is accelerating in order to improve training qualifications as in other countries in the EC.

Reform Calendar

1991-92 .... Infant Schooling (3 to 6 years, not- compulsory)
1992-93 .... Primary Education, first and second (age 6 to 8)
1993-94 .... Primary Education, third and fourth (age 8 to 10)
1994-95 .... Primary Education, fifth (age 10 to 11)
1995-96 .... Primary Education, sixth (age 11 to 12)
1996-97 .... Secondary Education, first (age 12 to 13)

CURRENT EDUCATIONAL SYSTEM

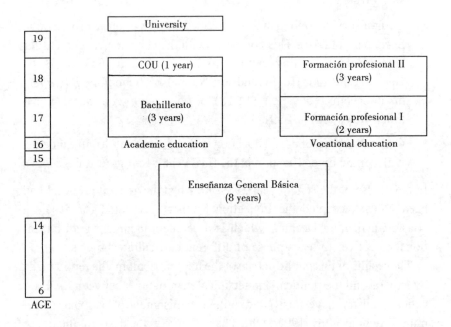

NEW EDUCATIONAL SYSTEM

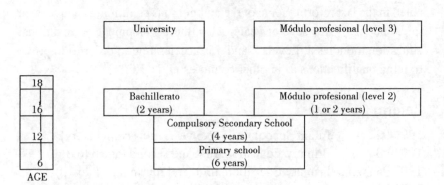

Figure 1

1997-98 .... Secondary Education, second (age 13 to 14)
1998-99 .... Secondary Education, third (age 14 to 15)
Secondary non-compulsory, first (age 16 to 17)
1999-2000 ..... Secondary Education, fourth (age 15 to 16)
Secondary non-compulsory, second (age 17 to 18)

At the present time and even for the next few years, the end of compulsory schooling of Spanish boys and girls (14 years) does not coincide with those of the other EC countries (usually 15 or 16 years) (see Chapter 1). This makes it difficult to set up comparisons of results for these ages because those few studies which exist, for example in general subjects and mathematics, usually focus on the end of an education period. But in Spain at present, at the end of compulsory schooling (14 years) students have three different routes. For example, figures from 1987-88 show the following:

14% of the students left the schooling system.
52% of the students continued to study in secondary schools.
34% of the students chose vocational education.

So the education system will gain comprehensively, because it will offer the same kind of schooling until 16 years of age. However it must be said that each of the present options for 14-16 years (*Bachillerato* and *Formación Profesional*) is comprehensive, especially for mathematics, because there is only one obligatory curriculum for all the students.

Curriculum and Evaluation in Mathematics: Reality and Perspectives

The future curriculum of Mathematics

The future mathematics curriculum focus has emerged from part of the experience in those schools in which the experimental reform was practised for 5 or 6 years. The most notable achievements have been retained but, at the same time, those deficiencies identified in numerous studies and meetings of teachers where the process was periodically evaluated, have been addressed.

Some of the general didactic and sociological essentials which inspire the next regional mathematics curriculum, and contained in the 'Minimum Teaching', obligatory for all Spanish regions, are:

- Mathematics must be presented as an essential skill to solve daily life situations, to aid better understanding of our own situations and to communicate and study other subjects.

- Secondary school mathematics curricula must centre on the acquisition of these basic capabilities needed for the formation of future citizens, and not merely on preparation for later studies.

- Mathematics curricula must include opportunities to learn general mathematical strategies, to work out, and to anticipate, problem-solving, to generalise and to apply, to explore patterns and relationships, etc. This is to help adaptation to new situations, essential in a society with constant changes.

- We must give students the opportunity to build their own mathematics knowledge, working at concrete problems which emphasise mathematical language and ideas. Not all students have to reach the same level of abstraction and formalisation at the end of compulsory schooling.

- It is essential for students to maintain a positive attitude to mathematics, allowing them to confront situations and trust in their own capacities.

The regional curricula will include the following:

1) Numbers and operations: Meanings, strategies and symbols.

2) Measurement, estimation and calculation.

3) Space: representation and organisation

4) Data: representation, interpretation and processing

5) Probability.

For methods of assessment, it is recommended that:

- Assessment should be understood as one of the phases of teaching and learning, as useful to students as to teachers, and inducting into the process of decision-taking.

226

- Such assessment should not be confused with the promotion of students from one year level to the next.

- Assessment should not be an isolated situation but made continuously throughout the year.

- Not only concepts and basic routines have to be assessed, but also general capabilities, modelling capacity, practice skills, attitudes towards mathematics.

- Student skills should be assessed in different situations and work contexts.

Mathematics as a subject will be common and obligatory to everybody throughout compulsory schooling with an allowance of 3 hours per week. A door has been left open in the last year of schooling (15-16 years), to allow a possibility for taking different levels, Mathematics A and B. The difference would be based on the kind of choices students are intending to make: *Bachillerato* technic-scientific or humanistic-linguistic, or vocational education.

Present Mathematics curriculum

The focus of the next mathematics curriculum contrasts strongly with the present syllabus in the first two years of secondary schooling (14-16 years). This is centred in the learning of a more abstract and arithmetical mathematics and in the training towards higher level studies. It is allowed 4 hours per week.

For example, the basic content of the current curriculum of secondary schooling for 14-16 years old, found in the majority of text books is:

- Academic study of numeracy.

- Algebra, centred in manipulation and not in creation but in the significance of letters and symbols.

- Analytical plane geometry.

- Trigonometry

- Lineal, quadratic, exponential, logarithmic and trigonometrical functions, from an algebraic view point.

- Functions and successive limits.

- Primitive and derivative function concepts.

- Combinatorics, probability and general statistics.

Let us remember that this syllabus is common and obligatory for all the students of *'Bachillerato'* (secondary schooling, 14-16 years). The vocational education mathematics syllabus is similar, although it is less extensive because it is only for the first course.

There are some recommendations and expectations for students' assessment of all subjects. It should help in the process of decision-taking, exemplifying the value of the chosen didactic style. However, more studies are needed to identify those capabilities and skills required for mathematics and the different methods by which they should be assessed.

We do not know any systematic study about different styles and assessment processes used in teachers' daily practices. But based on our collective experience, we can explain some of the characteristics of mathematical assessment of Spanish boys and girls between 14 and 16 years:

- Assessment affects the students' promotion from one course to the next depending on the marks obtained; very rarely are the marks accompanied by other more detailed written reports. Results have a minimum influence on syllabus change or didactic strategies of teachers.

- Assessment is made at isolated times (written exams between three and six times each year). If students do not pass, they have to retake. A pass is required to enable them to go to the next year of studies, or they have to repeat the whole year. The teachers do not usually find out the reasons for failure in order to help resolve students' difficulties.

- Examinations are related to the actual curriculum and common schooling practice; their content is basically arithmetic, depends on memorisation, and rarely contains interesting applied problems, small investigations, etc.

- Sometimes certain student activities are observed in the classroom, usually the most brilliant, the most spontaneous, the less capable... Generally a systematic observation of all students is not planned nor is account taken of classroom behaviour when teachers give students marks.

- Very few teachers look at students' notebooks or their practical work in relation to other subjects or at daily life, group activities, etc, nor is coursework used towards the evaluation in the teachers' final examinations.

In all subjects, students who do not pass a course, can take an exam in June after classes have finished, and can try again in the first days of September, before the beginning of the new school year. We show some exams for 1 º B.U.P. (15 years) and 2 º B.U.P. (16 years) in Appendix I. They are similar in all schools and students have two hours to answer them.

How do teachers feel about the innovations?

What is the Spanish mathematics' teachers position with regard to the changes which are coming? For teachers, the new educational system implies a lot of changes in working and professional conditions, salaries are unclear. Students are likely to come from different backgrounds and schools. The situation produces uneasiness and insecurity among all of us.

Mathematics curricular changes produce a wide range of opinions: hopeful and valued by the most progressive sectors; ambiguously by others who realise the inadequacy of the present syllabus in the classroom and the advance of mathematical education; and, finally, there is a small sector of teachers who are strongly against the new curriculum and who anticipate a fall in the quality and levels of teaching in the new syllabus and that the 'real sense' of mathematics will be lost. We all agree about the difficulties we have to face, and a lot of teachers feel insecure with some not well known new syllabus aspects (like geometry or statistics), and the recommended range of didactic methods.

Besides this, the most disturbing question, especially among the teachers familiar with the new curriculum, is assessment. Even those who do not agree with the present evaluation system, based only on academic examinations, have a lot of questions about the coming situation amongst which are:

- How can we observe and evaluate students' attitudes towards mathematics?

- What contexts and activities are adequate to assess problem solving?

- How can we test the capacity of students to transfer from school to daily life situations?

- How can we observe each student's behaviour in a working group, and the total group behaviour?

- How can our students' evaluations be used to help us improve our teaching, and their learning?

- What will be the relationship between assessment of students and teachers' promotion?

That is why assessment is one of the favourite topics in mathematics teachers' meetings. We recognise that we still have a lot to learn, experience and practice. As yet we do not have enough experience and investigation to show us how these changes affect context.

National examinations and performance studies

The present system does not have external examinations. This means that there are as many examinations as schools, and, in each school, as teachers. (Each University sets its own entrance examination). At the end of the school year each school must send their statistics obtained from the marks of their students to the Educational Administration, so that standards in Basic General Education can be monitored, in all subjects of secondary and vocational education.

However as details are not published and then only in a few cases is there differentiation by gender, we are unable to give a picture of mathematical performance at the end of compulsory schooling. In the second part of this chapter, therefore, we give the results of some particular studies into different aspects of the teaching and evaluation of mathematics. The only overall fact we can give about mathematics in secondary schooling is that there is about a 50% failure rate.

Girls' Position in the Current Education System

Girls' presence in the different age sectors

There is universal attendance at compulsory school called *Enseñanza General Básica* (EGB) from 6 to 14 years. The school population is distributed 48% female, 52% male. This proportion changes when the pupils pass into the non-compulsory sector. In *Bachillerato* (academic education) there are more girls than boys: 54% versus 46%. In *Formación Profesional* (vocational education) it is the opposite: there are more boys (58%) than girls.

This situation is in accord with the better results that, globally, girls obtain in the present compulsory school, because to go to *Bachillerato* a pupil needs to have obtained the title *Graduado Escolar,* which is not necessary for access to *Formación Profesional.*

In the university, female presence has increased spectacularly in the last fifteen years, and now it is a little more than 50%, but this still does not correspond to the 54% of pupils who are female achieving the *Bachillerato.*

Girls' curricular and professional choices

The data given above refer to the total of all specialities. When we examine the subjects or vocational education choices traditionally seen as male in the *Bachillerato,* where the choice of stream must be made at age sixteen, we find 48% female in the scientific stream, and 60% female in the literary or humanities. In the humanities stream pupils continue studying mathematics, but not physics or other scientific subjects.

In *Formación Profesional,* the stereotypes are reproduced in the branches girls and boys choose, though the situation has improved in the last few years. About 42% of pupils are female, but almost all are to be found studying Fashion and Clothing (90%), Hairdressing (86%), Sanitary (78%) and Administration (64%). In Metal (8.5%), Electricity (10.5%) and Mechanics (11%) their presence is clearly less.

At the university a situation similar to that in *Formación Profesional* obtains. In engineering only 13% of the students are female. The highest female rate is in the study of architecture (30%) and the lowest in aeronautics (2%).

with 72%), there is a roughly even distribution in mathematics, chemistry and biology, and the rate decreases in other scientific studies such as physics (28%). An inquiry made among female mathematics students revealed that their career expectations were almost 100% teaching, whereas their male colleagues opted for a broader range including research, business, etc.

Like those in other countries, we note that the least attractive option in *Bachillerato* is not mathematics alone, but the association mathematics-physics. We also note that only 39% of doctoral students overall are female.

Girls' Mathematics Achievement

Probably the first time attention was called to the performance differences between Spanish girls and boys in mathematics and science was the 'International Assessment of Educational Progress' (IAEP) made by the USA Educational Testing Service (ETS) in 1989. These results, made public but not sufficiently analysed, have alerted both administration and some teachers to the disparity in performance and has raised official interest in researching it.

Results and attitudes in compulsory school

In a study made by the CIDE (Educational Documentation and Investigation Centre) of a group at the end of compulsory school (14 years), (1989) the results were:

- School marks in mathematics and language are the lowest of all subjects. Each school has its own assessment style (and each teacher too) so they are non-comparable.

- Girls' mathematics school marks are slightly better than are boys'.

- A formal written examination was taken by the same students. Girls obtained better results than boys in calculation and worse in applied mathematics.

- In a standard capabilities test girls did worse in verbal and numeric factors, spatial ability and mechanical reasoning, but did a little better in abstract reasoning.

In spite of these better results at school, which are confirmed by some other studies and the opinions of teachers, girls have negative feelings and opinions about mathematics, as shown in a study done by researchers at Zaragoza University (Escudero, 1987):

- Students, both girls and boys, consider mathematics the most difficult subject, but the percentages are 51% of the girls and 29% of the boys.

- The most unpopular subjects are religion, languages (Spanish and foreign), and then mathematics. Nevertheless, asked about the most amusing subject, 12% of girls and 8% of boys answered mathematics.

- The majority of the students think that the most important subject is mathematics, 66% of boys and 49% of girls.

This and other studies confirm consistency with the international literature. Typically, girls believe they have little capability which is the cause of their failure, while hard work and luck are the cause of their success, the contrary to boys.

Secondary performances (sixteen years)

In Spain, the most far-reaching study made about sixteen year old students (at the end of the future compulsory school) was to evaluate the experimental reform of secondary schooling (Alvarez Page et al, 1990). A comparison was made with the actual school system. Students sat tests which showed the girls performing better than the boys in calculations but worse in mathematics applications. The experimental teaching did not improve the results in boys or girls, and both were slightly worse at calculations than those in the normal school setting (193-194). However other more open tests, which asked about mathematics capabilities (problem solving, critical attitude, use of different mathematical languages, ability to argue and explain) gave different results. In the normal setting boys out-performed girls in those kind of questions, but this was reversed in the experimental school students. In particular, girls in the experimental schools did better than those in the traditional. Unfortunately the evaluation was made with the kind of test usually set in the traditional system and, very different from the experimental assessment styles which included a broader range than simply unseen timed written tests. In particular, one finding was of note: the expectations of girls studying in the experimental schools were much higher than those in the traditional schools. 71% of them had ambitions to go to the university compared with 58% of the girls in traditional schools, and 50% would like to do a job which implies high responsibility and qualification (138, 199).

Reaching the University

One of the most complete examinations of students' performance from a gender perspective has been made on the marks from the university entrance examination (17-18 years) (Muñoz-Repiso, 1991). Some important characteristics of these examinations are:

- The exam is set by each university and usually consists of routine exercises and some conceptual or theoretical items covering all the subjects that the student does during the last year of Secondary school (*Curso de Orientación Universitaria*). (See appendix II for some examples).

- The mark awarded is the mean between the one awarded from the test, and the average of all the marks obtained by the student in her/his secondary school (four years).

- In the study no particular analysis of mathematics achievement alone was done, but in three of the four options possible in the final year of secondary school, students take mathematics. These are Scientific, Biosanitary and Social Sciences.

The analysis of the data shows that for these options:

- the average marks are slightly better for girls than for boys;
- the examination marks are worse for both girls and boys than their coursework marks;
- the girls' examination marks are slightly lower than the boys';
- the final calculated means permitting entry to University or not are worse for girls than for boys.

Differences of achievement in mathematics competition

A study was made by Fidela Velazquez in the Canary Islands over the last seven years based on performances in the mathematics competition which takes place at the end of the final year of compulsory schooling (fourteen years). The competition is organised by the Mathematics Teachers Canary Islands Association 'Isaac Newton', which invites all the schools from the Canary Islands, public and private, to participate. Similar competitions are held in other areas of Spain, followed by a national competition with the best from each area, organised by the Mathematics Teachers Associations National Federation. Each school sends one for every twenty pupils, and the chosen pupil is therefore the best in the class. All the selected pupils take an examination which is mainly about problem solving. In a second round, between ten and twenty of the best are chosen, and they take a final examination from which the three best are found.

There are always more boys participating in the competition than girls, which contradicts the expected situation since normally, at that age, girls reach higher levels of qualification than boys. One possible explanation is that fewer girls than boys wish to accept the offer of a chance to participate. When the results of the finalists are analysed, boys have a much higher pass rate, and more boys pass to the second round than girls. The results are significantly better for the boys.

Although further studies are required, the lower achievement of girls in this kind of competition may be due to:

- Girls' lesser beliefs in their own performances;

- Problem solving being a habit. Boys practice for hours of every day of every year in their lives; for example when mending a bicycle boys think constructively about it;

- The kind of problems set in the competition might be more familiar to boys than girls. This needs investigating;

- Girls not liking to compete.

The more competitive international competition is the International Mathematics Olympiad where the problems posed have a high level of abstraction and formalisation. We do not have data from local participation, but no girl has participated in the Ibero-american competition, and overall only 5% of participants are female.

Teachers and girls

Some studies confirm results found in other countries (Alberdi and Escario, 1985-86). Teachers do not recognise the existence of sexist attitudes in classrooms or schools; they affirm that girls obtain better marks than boys (which is true). Nevertheless, when teachers are observed in classrooms, they give girls less attention and have a lower estimation of their abilities than those of the boys (ibid, p.112-113).

Conclusions

From the above we can conclude that:

- girls' results under conditions of continuous assessment are better but boys performance is better on timed, unseen written paper and pencil tests;

- when assessment includes a wider range of mathematical behaviours than simply algorithmic knowledge and skills girls improve their achievement;

- girls take part in non-competitive tasks more spontaneously;

- girls feel less confident with mathematics than boys, in spite of their better marks;

- girls tend to take options without mathematics, which blocks access to scientific and technical studies or employment. Some studies (Muñoz-Repiso, *et al* 1992) point out that the association mathematics-physics is the least attractive.

We emphasise that these conclusions must be treated as provisional and that it is necessary to design specific research to establish significant relationships between assessment styles and girls' mathematics achievement. Clear results would help to destroy the myth of female mathematical inferiority. It would be interesting to analyse the influence of that prejudice on girls' low attribution of mathematical abilities and in their resultant choice of technical or non-technical careers.

Bibliography

Alberdi, I., Escario, P. (1985-86) 'La persistencia del sexismo en la Enseñanza Media. Actitudes de los profesores'. C.I.D.E., Madrid.

Alvarez Page, M., et al (1990) 'Evaluación externa de la Reforma Experimental de las Enseñanzas Medias II'. Ministerio de Educación y Ciencia, C.I.D.E., Madrid.

Centro Nacional de Investigación y Documentación Educativa, Instituto de la Mujer (1988) 'La presencia de las mujeres en el sistema educativo'. Madrid.

Escudero Escorza, T. (1987) 'El paso de la E. G. B. a las E. E. M. M. Trauma o liberación'. C.I.D.E. Madrid.

Instituto de la Mujer (1992) *La Mujer en Cifras*, Madrid.

Lapointe, A.E., Mead, N.A., Philips, G.W. (1989) 'Un mundo de diferencias: Un estudio Internacional de Evaluación de las Matemáticas y las Ciencias'. C.I.D.E. Madrid.

Ministerio de Educación y Ciencia (1989) 'Libro blanco para la Reforma del Sistema Educativo'. Madrid.

Ministerio de Educación y Ciencia (1991) 'Estadística de la Enseñanza en España 1987/88' Madrid.

Muñoz-Repiso, M., et al. (1991) 'Las calificaciones en las pruebas de aptitud para el acceso a la Universidad'. Ministerio de Educación y Ciencia, C.I.D.E., Madrid.

Muñoz-Repiso, M., et al. (1992) 'El sistema educativo español 1991'. Ministerio de Educación y Ciencia, Centro de Investigación, Documentación y Evaluación. Madrid.

SUFICIENTCIA

1º B.U.P.

1) Calcular $-2\sqrt{150}+\dfrac{3}{5}\sqrt{54}+\dfrac{1}{3}\sqrt{96}$

y además racionalizar $\dfrac{3}{2\sqrt{2}-\sqrt{5}}$

2) Efectuar la suma $\dfrac{6}{x}-\dfrac{x}{x+1}-\dfrac{3x-3}{x^2-1}$

3) Factorizar el polinomio $x^5-x^4-4x^3+4x^2$

4) Resolver el sistema $\begin{cases} x+2y=5 \\ x^2+xy=3 \end{cases}$

5) Descomponer el número 500 en dos partes (dos números), de modo que al dividir la mayor entre la menor se obtenga de cociente 7 y de resto 20.

6) En la ecuación $x^2-2x+a=0$ hallar el valor de "a" para que:
   (i) las dos raíces sean iguales
   (ii) una raíz sea el doble de la otra.

7) Resolver la ecuación $\sqrt{x+2}+x=2x-4$

8) Efectuar el desarrollo de $(x^2-\dfrac{2}{x})^5$

9) Representar gráficamente la parábola $y=-x^2+2x-3$.

10) Resolver la inecuación $5x^2-6x+1 < 0$

SUFICIENCIA

2º B.U.P.

1) Sea la sucesión $0, \dfrac{3}{5}, \dfrac{8}{10}, \dfrac{15}{17}, \ldots\ldots$

  (a) Hallar el término general y el término de lugar 100

  (b) Representar gráficamente sus términos

  (c) Estudiar si es acotada y hallar el límite.

2) Calcular el Lím. $\left(\dfrac{2n-1}{2n+1}\right)^{-2n^2}$

3) Resolver $3^{x+1} - 2.3^x - 2.3^{x-1} = 81$

4) Calcular $\displaystyle\lim_{x\to-3} \dfrac{x^3+5x^2+3x-9}{x^3+7x^2+15x+9}$

5) Resolver la ecuación $4\log x - \log\left(x^2-\dfrac{4}{5}\right) = \log 5$

6) Sabiendo que la $Tag\, x = \dfrac{3}{4}$ ($180 < x < 270$), hallar las demás razones

trigonométricas así como el valor de $Tag(180-x)$.

7) Calcular $\displaystyle\lim_{x\to 0} \sqrt{x}\,(\sqrt{x+1} - \sqrt{x-1})$

8)   Una escalera de 10m. de longitud, colocada en un determinado punto fijo de la calzada de una calle, puede apoyarse sobre una fachada formando con el suelo un ángulo de 30º y un ángulo de 60º con otra fachada de la miema calle.¿ Cuál es la anchura de la escalera?¿ Cuál es la altura que la escalera alcanza sobre cada fachada?

9)   Dada la recta que corta a los ejes en los puntos A(3,0) y B(0,-2), hallar:

  (a) Sus ecuaciones paramétricas y su ecuación general

  (b) La ecuación de la paralela que pasa por el punto C(-3,-1)

10) Sean $\vec{a}\,(1, -1)\, y\, \vec{b}\,(2, -4)$. Estudier si son linealmente inde-

pendientes. Escribir $\vec{c}\,(5,7)$ como combinación lineal de a y b.

PRUEBAS DE ACCESO A LA UNIVERSIDAD

MATERIA: Matemáticas I (Obligatoria)

TIEMPO: Una hora treinta minutos

INSTRUCCIONES: El alumno elegirá libremente DOS de las cuatro cuestiones que se presentan a continuación y dará respuestas razonadas claras y concisas a las partes a) y b) de que constan las cuestiones escogidas.

CUESTION 1

a) Dada la matriz $A = \begin{pmatrix} 2 & 3 \\ 1 & 2 \end{pmatrix}$, hallar una matriz X tal que

$$AXA = \begin{pmatrix} 1 & 1 \\ 2 & 3 \end{pmatrix}$$

b) Determinar a y b para que sea continua la función

$$f(x) = \begin{cases} x^2 + 1 & \text{si} & x < 0 \\ ax + b & \text{si} & 0 \leq x \leq 3 \\ x - 5 & \text{si} & x > 3 \end{cases}$$

¿La función que resulta es derivable en $x = 3$?

CUESTION 2

a) Calcular el volumen del cuerpo que se obtiene al hacer girar la curva $y = \dfrac{1}{\sqrt{2 + x^2}}$ en torno al eje OX, entre $x = 0$ y $x = \sqrt{2}$.

b) Se consideran el plano $\pi : 2x - y + z + 1 = 0$, la recta $s : x - 3y = 0$, $z = 1$ y el punto $A(4, 0, -1)$. Hallar el plano que pasa por A, es paralelo a la recta s y perpendicular al plano π.

CUESTION 3

a) Se tienen tres sucesos A, B, C de un experimento aleatorio, con $P(A) = 0.7$, $P(B) = 0.6$, $P(C) = 0.1$, $P(A^c \cup B^c) = 0.58$. Se pide
  1) ¿Son independientes A y B?
  2) ¿Cuál es el valor máximo que puede tomar $P(A \cap C)$?. Si toma ese valor máximo, calcular $P(C^c / A^c)$. (A^c significa complementario de A).

b) Dada la función $f(x) = \dfrac{1}{x} + L(x)$ hallar
  1) Dominio de existencia.
  2) Representación gráfica. ($L(x)$ =logaritmo neperiano de x).

CUESTION 4

a) Hallar la proyección del punto $P(2, -1, 3)$ sobre la recta

$$r : \begin{cases} x = 3t \\ y = 5t - 7 \\ z = 2t + 2 \end{cases}$$

y hallar la distancia de P a r.

b) Discutir el sistema según los valores del parámetro a y resolverlo cuando sea compatible

$$\left. \begin{array}{r} -x - \quad y - z = -2 \\ (a-1)x + (a-1)y - 2z = -2 \\ ax + (a+1)y \quad = 1 \end{array} \right\}$$

240

CHAPTER ELEVEN

Sweden

Barbro Grevholm
Margita Nilsson

Sweden has a national curriculum and a relative marking system from the 8th school year. The marks are 1-5 and 5 is the best. At the end of Comprehensive School, there is a national standardised test to help teachers find the level for the average value 3. In the tests boys score higher than girls, but in spite of that girls get better end of term marks than boys. The texts of the tests are kept secret by the National Board of Education, but we have been allowed to quote the tests from 1990. We give a general view of Swedish investigations into gender differences in mathematics. In the near future, many things in Swedish schools are going to change. There will be a new school organisation, new curricula and perhaps a new marking system.

Background

In Sweden, the Comprehensive School started about 1969. Children begin school at seven and there are nine grades. The school system is centralised and there is a national curriculum. The schools are communal and very few private schools exist. However, this system is going to change and a debate is going on. The government now wants a decentralised system, result-oriented and controlled through evaluation based on formulated goals.

Mathematics is studied by everybody in all the nine grades, for 3-4 lessons a week. The school year consists of about 36 effective weeks. Usually the pupils do a very small amount of homework.

At the end of Compulsory School, the pupils in Sweden get a school based leaver's certificate, showing their results graded 1-5. There is no formal examination. The marking system is a relative system, where the control group consists of all the pupils in grade nine that year. The assumption is that the results are normally distributed, and the results, for the whole country, should be spread like this:

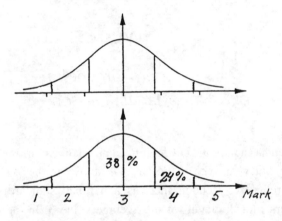

The teacher decides the marks with the help of standardised national tests. The number of pupils given mark 3 should therefore exceed the number of pupils awarded marks 4-5 and the number of those given marks 1-2. The ideal statistical average is 3.0. As the marks 1-5 should as far as possible be the same all over the country, the teacher needs some help to decide what should be demanded for a mark of 3. Therefore, there is a general assessment by standardised tests in the last term of Grade 9. These tests are called Standard tests (National Board of Education, 1985).

Standard tests

It is compulsory for all schools to participate in the standard tests and to send a sample of the pupils' results to the Board of Education in Stockholm. Actually 80% of the schools do this. Then all schools get information about the average in the country and about the upper and lower limit for the grade 3. This grade thereby includes some 40% of the pupils. The tests take place in March/April. The schools can choose the date. They do not all have to do it on the same day.

This general assessment is official but neither the tests nor particular results are published. These are kept secret. There are many reasons for this, the most important perhaps being that not too much attention should be given to assessment. On the other hand, critics claim that everything should be discussed openly, and the reason for not doing so might be that the results are too bad. In spite of this, we have been permitted to include in this chapter the test results from 1990 and 1991.

In Sweden there are two mathematics curricula for the grades 7-9, one less and one more advanced. The less advanced is called General Course (GC) and the more demanding Advanced Course (AC). About 60% of the pupils in grade 9 chose the Advanced Course. The number of lessons are the same for both courses.

There used to be gender differences in the choice of mathematics courses. In the mid seventies, there were fewer girls who chose the advanced course, but by the mid eighties the choices were equally distributed across the sexes. In terms of distribution, therefore, the only difference is that fewer boys than girls from working class families tend to choose the advanced course. However, in the 7th school year, 30% of the boys but only 3% of the girls choose science as a voluntary subject.

There are two standard tests, one for each curriculum. Both tests consist of two parts. An example of a test for the Advanced Course is included as Appendix 0.

Part 1
40 minutes; no calculators

This part consists of 20 questions. For 15 of them, only an answer is demanded, for the rest a solution should also be given. The pupils are recommended to use mental calculations as much as possible. Typical items concern numerical calculations, percentages, diagrams, equations, geometry, algebra, proportionality. The questions that demand solutions are always textual problems.

Part 2

75 minutes; calculators allowed

This part is based on a theme. The pupil gets a booklet of 5-6 pages where the theme is presented. Text, pictures, diagrams and tables give many data from which the pupils may choose. About 13 questions are posed where the pupil has to look for relevant information in the booklet and then carry out some calculations. This implies that all the questions must lead to ordinary everyday mathematics. It is, for example, difficult to find pure algebra in it.

In our opinion, the tests cover the core of each curriculum very well and allow pupils with more knowledge to show this. The range of difficulty is perhaps a little different compared to Finland and Norway, but in many respects there is a similarity between these three countries.

As a result of the change of education system the standardised tests are probably going to disappear. What is going to replace them is now being discussed, as is also the content of the curriculum and the marking system.

Results of standard tests — Gender difference

Before completing the construction of the tests, the items are tested on some hundreds of pupils. They give an average of about half of 45 maximum points available (see Table page 245).

In both years, the boys score higher in tests, but the girls are given higher grades by their teachers although the difference is small. In the information to schools, it is pointed out that the difference in grades given by teachers to boys and girls does not correspond with the test results.

Comments

It is difficult to explain the differences between test results and marks. Maybe the marks are as fair as they can be, when everything teachers know, written and oral, is taken into account. Maybe teachers tend in some respects to overvalue the girls. The situation is complex and no conclusions can be drawn. Nevertheless we will comment on this question below.

In the first place, we would like to quote from the Comprehensive School Curriculum:

General Course (GC)			
		Girls (49%)	Boys (51%)
1990	Average in tests	25.7	25.9
	Average teacher grade	3.05	2.86
		Girls (47%)	Boys (53%)
1991	Average in tests	21.7	22.9
	Average teacher grade	3.02	2.84
Advanced Course (AC)			
		Girls (50%)	Boys (50%)
1990	Average in tests	23.3	26.0
	Average teacher grade	3.25	3.18
		Girls (50%)	Boys (50%)
1991	Average in tests	22.9	25.2
	Average teacher grade	3.24	3.19
Standard deviation is about 0.9 for marks and about 10-11 for tests results.			

Marks in certain subjects, where written tests are given, should not depend only on these tests. All achievements are to be included and the teacher must avoid overvaluing some results that are easier to judge than are others (National Board of Education, 1980).

The results on the standard test should not decide the end of school mark of the pupil. It is possible that judgement of the whole achievement of the pupil is one reason why the marks for girls are better than the results of the written tests.

Second, it is interesting to note that the situation is not subject specific. It has been shown in many other investigations in Swedish, Mathematics and in English that girls always get better marks than their results in written tests would predict. (See Emanuelsson and Fishbein, 1986). This study is quoted below.

Third, are the items in the standard tests gender-neutral? They seem to be. Almost all items have a neutral context or no context. One year, perhaps a theme like 'Building a house' may not appeal to girls, but then, why should not a girl do some calculations in connection with making a book-shelf, or try to find out how much material she needs for curtains? Besides another year the theme might appeal less to boys.

Most teachers seem to appreciate the existence of standard tests. They follow small changes in the content of the tests, thus influencing their own tests and their way of teaching. There has not been much discussion about the form and the content of the tests. Most teachers seem to think the tests are well constructed and it is acceptable that they are compulsory. Without interfering too much in the detail, the tests give the teachers support when they have to decide about marks.

Gender differences in other investigations

There have been many investigations concerning gender differences in assessment.

Bengt-Olov Ljung (1965) found a higher average in mathematics and a greater standard deviation among adolescent boys than girls. He found similar results when investigating the knowledge of mathematics among teacher trainees (1987).

IEA tests were conducted in Sweden in 1964 and 1980, in both compulsory schools and upper secondary schools (Matematik i Skolan, 1986). In both tests the boys' score is higher.

It is interesting to note that differences between classroom grades and the results of standardised tests have been reported by many researchers. Meredith Kimball (1989) examined some 150 studies on gender-related differences in mathematics achievement. Girls were, in most cases, reported to perform better on classroom tests than on standardised tests. She attempted to explain this but concluded that there is a need for more evidence before we can explain sex-related differences between classroom and standardised achievement measures. It seems to be an interesting research question which would require the gathering of more empirical evidence to evaluate different hypotheses to explain this situation. In Sweden, recent results from Prim-gruppen (Oscarsson, 1993) show that in upper secondary schools, the situation with classroom marks and test results is the same as described here for compulsory school.

Diagnostic tests in Upper Secondary School

At the start of upper secondary school pupils choose between a 2 year or a 3 year course. (In the near future this may change as all school education after compulsory school might be extended to 3 years). Usually the pupils with General Course in mathematics in compulsory school behind them, choose 2 years of further study, while most of those who have Advanced Course choose 3 years. Many pupils are given a diagnostic test, produced in co-operation with teachers by the National Board of Education to find out who needs help at the start of their new course. The tests cover most parts of the curriculum but they concentrate on basic concepts. There are different diagnostic tests for the 2 year and the 3 year groups. Recently, results from ten schools (not randomly chosen) have been published by the PRIM group at the Teacher Training College in Stockholm (Oscarsson, Rosén and Ljung, 1990a, 1990b).

These show:

2 years Upper Secondary School

80 minutes; no calculators

	General Course		Advanced Course	
	Boys	Girls	Boys	Girls
Number	737	355	374	240
Average (Max 50)	18.6	21.0	32.7	32.3
Standard deviation is about 9-10				

Among those pupils who took the General Course in compulsory school, girls score higher; the gender difference on average is greater than for those who took the Advanced Course in compulsory school.

3-years Upper Secondary School

In the 3 year group, only 6% of the participants had GC in compulsory school. We omit these and give the results only for those with AC.

	Girls	Boys
Number	367	389
Average (Max 60)	36.7	40.4
Standard deviation is about 9-10		

Here the boys score more. In some more detail, the result is shown below:

Fig 5. Total points in percentage for boys and girls with AC.
(Taken from Oscarsson, Rosen and Ljung, 1990b)

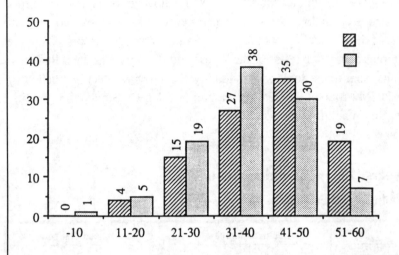

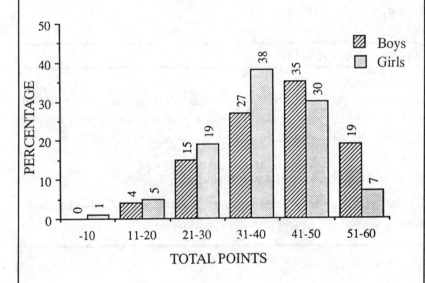

University Entrance Examination

In Sweden there is a general test called the University Entrance Examination. Even if your marks from Upper Secondary School are not sufficient, this test may open the door to university studies for you, if your result is good. The University Entrance Examination is an important test and the importance is increasing. The average result of the University Entrance Test is 1.2 for men and 1.0 for women, out of a maximum of 2.0 points. The test includes, among many other things, two parts which test the ability to read diagrams and maps and to think in a logical fashion. In these two parts of the test, the greatest gender differences appear, and, in them, there is no single item in which women score higher than men (Ljung, G. 1990).

When some years ago gender differences in the results were observed, a debate started. Critics claim that multiple choice questions and questions where you just mark with an x should, at least, be replaced. Participants should either give written answers or draw pictures. Some people thought that as marks at school were in favour of girls, it was a good thing that this test was in favour of boys. Other demanded that the test be examined and changed to give equal results for both sexes.

Sex and Schooling

In 'Vive la Difference? A Study of Sex and Schooling', Emanuelsson and Fischbein (1986) give a summary of earlier research in Sweden concerning gender differences in marks and test results. We quote this investigation at some length and start with a table for results in mathematics. All differences are presented in standard deviation units.

In all investigations the boys scored higher, with one exception in 1981 where there is no difference. In spite of the test results girls in most cases achieved better marks than boys.

Emanuelsson and Fischbein also show results from two other subjects, Swedish and English. In Swedish girls have better test results than boys but even better marks. In English boys have better test results but girls have better marks.

Thus the same trend of difference between written tests and marks appears in all these three subjects, always with the marks better for girls,

Table 1: Differences* (standard deviation units) presented in Swedish studies between girls and boys for marks and test results in Swedish, Mathematics and English.

Subject	Source	Year of study	Grade	Marks	Test results
Maths	Individual statistics (Svensson, 1971)	1961	6 (elementary) (comprehensive)	.01 .00	-.18 -.17
	Orebro-project (Bergman, 1978)	1965	3	-.05	-.12
	Individual statistics (Svensson, 1971)	1966	6 (elementary) (comprehensive)	.11 .01	-.08 -.17
	VMU-project (Carlsten, 1971)	1966	9 (general) (elementary)	.04 -.07	-.20 -.36
	Orebo-project (Bergman, 1978)	1968	6	.05	-.12
	Orebo-project (Bergman, 1978)	1970	8 (general) (advanced)	.36 .11	- -
	Segregation project (Andersson et al, 1983)	1978	6	.10**	
	Segregation project (Andersson et al, 1983)	1981	9 (general) (advanced)	.20** .10**	.00** .00**
*	Positive differences = higher average scores for girls than for boys Negative differences = higher average scores for boys than for girls				
**	Approximation				

the test results for boys. This is an interesting observation, worth further investigation.

In their discussion, Emanuelsson and Fischbein pose three questions:

1. Are sex differences for marks and test results of the same magnitude in the 196's and in 1980?

2. Are sex differences for marks and test results of the same magnitude at different ages?

3. Are sex differences for marks in relation to test results related to common home and classroom environments?

Their answers are:

1. In the 1960s boys had better test results than girls and they also had somewhat better marks. In 1980 the differences in test results had almost vanished, but now in spite of somewhat better test results for boys the girls have even better marks.

2. Girls gain higher marks at the age of 16 than at the age of 12.

3. The main source of variance is sex for both test results and marks.

Are trends like these to be found in other countries? It would be an interesting question to investigate.

Another interesting question is what happens to the marks of the girls after 16 years of age, at the Upper Secondary School level.

What Mathematics do girls choose in Upper Secondary School?

What mathematics course do girls choose after leaving the comprehensive school? In Sweden there are four possible mathematics curricula at the Upper Secondary School level. The most advanced course is included in the science and technology programme, whereas the program with society and economics as main subject contains a less advanced course in mathematics. The two year programmes include the simplest course. In some of the two year programmes it is currently possible to take no mathematics but this is going to change and, in future, all students will have a compulsory mathematics course.

The total number of pupils in Grade 9 is about 100,000. In 1990, those entering 3 years of Upper Secondary Education chose mathematics as follows

	Girls	Boys
Most advanced Maths (Science and Technology)	6,900	13,600
Less advanced Maths (Society and Economics)	15,400	8,800

Thus in Sweden about 45% of the girls chose a demanding mathematics course. At the same time it should be noted that only about 14% of the girls chose the science line, and many of them do this out of an interest in biology and chemistry, not in physics or mathematics. Those who choose the less advanced mathematics course, do not choose for the sake of mathematics and usually have little interest in this subject. Many of the girls who choose a two year study program want to avoid mathematics. It would be interesting to do some research about the attitudes behind these choices. It is extremely difficult to attract girls to studies including more mathematics, especially since choices reflect feelings, attitudes, and interests which currently lead in different directions.

Girls in the world of School mathematics

We now address some aspects of what girls may feel when working in the textbook world of mathematics, given that this is the predominant style of classroom working.

Invisible girls

In 1987, Mats Areskoug and Barbro Grevholm pointed out that girls were made invisible in the textbook world of mathematics in Sweden. First names of boys and figures of boys were twice as common as those of girls. Since then, things have improved and some authors now take care to show girls. But even today the context is often either neutral or concerns, say, sports liked by boys, whereas there is not much to which girls can relate. Very few problems in the texts concern something positive for girls. Grevholm and Areskoug also asked why mathematics textbooks do not treat more interesting and serious problems like the important survival questions of the human race. We all know that pupils in their teens are very concerned about these questions. Now they are often asked to calculate how much they will save buying a packet of margarine of one size instead of another. But also in this respect, things are improving. Some new textbooks contain better problems.

Pseudo problems

A kind of pseudo problem appears in most textbooks (Bratt, Grevolm & Nilsson, 1988). You are not only asked to calculate about packets of margarine. The problem may concern for example making a meal for 4 persons instead of 6, and instead of getting interested in calculations a sensible person might think 'I will make it for 6, the leftovers we can use tomorrow or then I will put them into the freezer'. The effect of this is unknown, but there may be an effect, especially felt by those who do not take an interest in mathematics. Thus their interest may not be awakened, and on the contrary, they may conclude that they can do without mathematics and turn to other things.

Impersonal Mathematics

By tradition, mathematics in textbooks is impersonal, not only when triangles and things like that are concerned (Ibid). Someone buys something, the price of something increases, but one does not know anything more about the situation as this is mathematically irrelevant. A hypothesis could be made that this is not enough for those girls who might need a less impersonal context to awaken their interest, or at least to help them feel less outside in this impersonal world. Clearly mathematics in the long run is impersonal, although its applications often have very personal implications. However, the point is what you feel when you are or you are not attracted to the subject.

Questions of your own

The range of problems in the textbooks is rather narrow. There are not many suggestions for investigation to be made, and in the grades 7-9 very little material of an experimental or laboratory character (Areskoug & Grevholm, 1987). In the lower grades, this is much better, but then pupils also like mathematics in these grades. Usually, after they are 13 years old, the pupils are asked to read the problems in the textbook and answer questions posed to them. They are not asked to find out for themselves what they need to solve a problem, much less to pose a problem themselves and ask their own questions. All this, as is well known, tends to make pupils passive. No one gains and certainly not girls.

Wish to avoid competition

Many investigations seem to confirm that girls like to co-operate with others while boys like competition. Many girls say they feel stressed and frustrated at test situations. Mathematics tests in Sweden are arranged so that they are very like a competition. Time usually is an important factor. It has been shown that girls want to think things through and not rush, while boys are happier to give a quick answer and like to be in a competitive situation when time is short (Staberg, 1992). It could be important to find out whether other test arrangements would fit both sexes better. Further research concerning these questions should be carried out.

Lack of self-confidence?

Very often, it seems to be assumed that girls lack self- confidence. It is a great problem if they do. But it does not follow that if girls thought 'I can do it!', they would immediately take an interest in mathematics. Many girls know they can, but they do not want to. They might ask: Why Mathematics at all?

An example may suffice to throw some light on the question. A familiar textbook problem asks pupils to find out, from some given figures, how many illiterates there are in the world. This did not interest one class of girls who said:

> Of course it is easy to do the calculation. But WHY should we do it? It is evident that the illiterates are too many. So what is one going to do? What does it help to calculate how many there are?

This goes back to the question of suitable problems. But the question: Why use Mathematics? should also be answered to respond to the conditions. In this connection it could also be noted, that many teachers in grades 1-6, doing in-service training, have admitted that they never knew WHY they were supposed to calculate a lot of things but just supposed it should be done and that someone else knew why.

Concluding remarks about assessment

In Sweden, there has been a debate about many school questions, including the marking system. But there has been no debate of importance concerning different kinds of assessment. We quote only two opinions commonly heard.

First, why is an assessment made? In Sweden, a lot of work is done to differentiate students by different marks. Maybe this is imposed by the university because of student demand for places. However, in Sweden, almost everyone after compulsory school finds a place somewhere for further school studies.

Also it frequently happens that students are placed in a study program not requested simply because there is a vacancy, and quite independently of their graded school results. In this case it is reasonable to ask why the grading?

Second, assessments should not be separated from school work. Would it not be wiser to give pupils of different ability and interest different work to do and consequently different forms of assessment? Thereby, the interests of all the pupils could be taken into account. An assessment could be given in the form of a certificate. Some of the certificates could be difficult to get, thereby showing a difference in quality. But for many kinds of further education, a certain amount of knowledge is demanded, not graded marks simply for their own sake.

References

Areskoug, M. & Grevholm, B. (1987) *Matematikgranskning,* Stockholm: SIL

Bratt, H., Grevholm, B. & Nilsson, M. (1988) *Den omöjliga läroboken*, Ds 1988:24, Stockholm.

Emanuelsson, J. & Fischbein, S. (1986) Vive la Difference? A Study in Sex and Schooling in *Scandinavian Journal of Educational Research*, 30, nr 2, 71-84.

Kimball, M. (1989) A new perspective on women's math achievement in *Psychological Bulletin,* 105 (2), 198-214.

Ljung, B-O (1965) *The adolescent Spurt in mental growth*. Stockholm: Almgvist & Wiksell.

Ljung, B-O (1987) *Klasslärarkandidaters räkneförmåga*. Stockholm: Högskolan för lärarutbildning.

Ljung, G. (1990) *Centrala prov i matematik, åk 3 NT,* Stockholm: Primgruppen.

Matematik i skolan (1986). Utbildningsdepartementet, DsU 1986:5, Stockholm Liber.

National Board of Education (1980) *Lgr 80* (The compulsory school curriculum), Stockholm: Utbildningsförlaget.

National Board of Education (1985) *Assessment in Swedish Schools,* Stockholm.

Oscarsson, E., Rosén, B. & Ljung, B-O (1990a) *Översiktsdiagnos i matematik inför skolstarten på tvååriga linjer*, Stockholm: Primgruppen.

Oscarsson, E. Rosén, B. & Ljung, B-O (1990b) *Översiktsdiagnos i matematik inför skolstarten på treåriga linjer*, Stockholm: Primgruppen.

Oscarsson, E. (1993) *Centrala prov i matematik, åk3SE*. Prim- gruppen (personal communication, not published).

Staberg, E-M (1992) *Olika världar, skilda värderingar. Hur flickor och pojkar möter högstadiets fysik, kemi och teknik*, Umeå: Pedagogiska Institutionen.

Standard Test in Mathematics
Advanced Course
Grade 9

Test 1

The test consists of two parts.
Part A: Answers only. A correct answer gives 1 mark.
Part B: Complete solutions to be given on squared paper. A correctly executed solution
          gives 2 marks per problem. The unit should always be stated in the answer.
          No mark if only the answer is given Aid: ruler.

A.   To the items 1-12 answers only

1   What is the price of a piece of ham weighing 6 hg if the price per kilogram
    is 150 kronor?

2   48/0.4

3   Simplify as far as possible 6x + 8y - 3x - 9y

4   What is the average speed in kilometers per hour of a cyclist who covers 8 km
    in 20 minutes?

5   $5.3 \cdot 10^3 + 4 \cdot 10^2$

6   A class was given the following problem:

    *1 kg of chocolates cost a kronor. Write down an
    expression for the cost of 2 hg of the chocolates.*

    Among the following five answers one is wrong. Ring the wrong answer.

    $\frac{a}{5}$ kr   0,2a kr $\frac{1}{5} \cdot a$ kr $\frac{1}{5a}$ kr $\frac{2a}{10}$ kr

7   Determine the value of the expression $\sqrt{9p^2} - 5$ for p = 2

8   Astrid buys a box of thin tiles. The tiles are squared with a side of 1 dm. Each box
    contains 3 m². How many tiles go into one box?

9   Insert the right sign + - • or / in the empty squares:

    14 ☐ 7 ☐ 2 ☐ 3 = 13

10   ROAD TRAFFIC DISCHARGE OF NITROGEN OXIDE IN 1000'S OF TONS

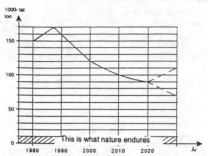

The Parliament has decided on a reduction by 30% reckoned on the 1980 discharge. Approximately when is that goal going to be reached?

11   The sum of all the angles in a polygon with n sides is 180(n-2) degrees. Determine this sum for a heptagon (7 sides)

12   One week at the end of a winter with very little snow a sport shop advertised:

> Ski sale!
> 20% reduction
> on all skis

The next week the shop advertised:

> Today clearence sale!
> All skis
> at half the sale price!

Now you seize the opportunity and buy a pair of skis. How large is the reduction in percent of the original price?

Part B.
To the items 13 - 17 complete solutions should be given.
Note! Only an answer gives no mark.

13   Solve the equation $3x + 4 = 7x - 1$

14   A skateboard team order a club-badge in the form of a dragon's head punched out of gold foil. They have to pay per square centimetre. How large is the area of the badge? (Tongue and flames are not counted)

15   Solve the equation $(3x + 1)^2 - 3(3x^2 + 2) = 7$

16   Simplify as far as possible $\dfrac{2a + b}{4a^2} \cdot \dfrac{16a}{2a + b}$

17   A window (see the figure) is composed of a square and a semicircle. Write an expression for the circumference of the window.

257

Standard Test in Mathematics
Advanced Course
Grade 9

Test 2

Theme Sri Lanka

Complete solutions to be given. A correct solution gives 2 marks.
No mark if only an answer is given. The unit should always be
stated in the answer. Aid: Calculator and ruler.

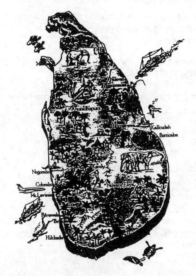

Sri Lanka is a country to the south-east of India. Formerly it was called Ceylon.
The capital is called Columbo. Sri Lanka has a tropical climate. The country is known for
its precious stones and famous for its fine tea. People also grow rice and have large
rubber plantations. For a long time the island of Sri Lanka has, however, been a popular
travel destination for Europeans. At present there are disturbances between different
ethnic groups.

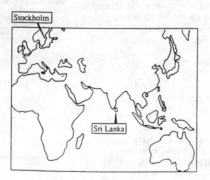

CLIMATE

1   The average temperature in Columbo i 81° F. How many degrees Celcius is that?
    Round off the result to whole degrees.

$$F = 1,8 \cdot C + 32$$
$$F = \text{Fahrenheit}$$
$$C = \text{Celsius}$$

POPULATION

Facts about Sri Lanka:
Population 1 jan 1988: 16.5 millions
Population growth/year: 1.4%
Inhabitants/km^2: 242

Facts about Sweden
Population 1 jan 1988: 8.4 millions
Area: 450 000 km^2

Ethnic groups in Sri Lanka 1988:

▤ Sinhalese,
☐ Tamils,
☐ Others

2   How many more inhabitants per square kilometre
    lived in Sri Lanka than in Sweden 1 jan 1988?

3   Determine the population growth in Sri Lanka
    from 1 jan 1988 to 1 jan 1991.
    Round off to hundreds of thousands .

4   The population is composed of various ethnic
    groups. Estimate how many millions of
    Sinhalese there were on 1 jan 1988.
    Do not forget to describe your line of thought.

ECONOMY

Production and commerce
in 1000's of tons in 1986

Goods	Production	Import	Export
Rice	1700	182	
Tea	215	-	198
Rubber	145	-	-

5   How large was the part of the tea production that was used within the country in
    1986? Answer in whole percentages.

6   A tea picker in Sri Lanka on average picks 20 kg of tea in a day. Her pay for that corresponds to 3 Swedish kronor. The kilogram price of tea in Sweden is 100 kronor. How many percent of the Swedish kilogram price constitute the pay she gets for picking 1 kg of tea?

7   Rice plants must grow on fields covered by water. How many cubic metres of water must be let out on a rice field of 0.6 hectares if the water level is to be raised by 15 cm? (1 hectare = 10 000 square metres)

8   2.5 kg of rubber can be tapped from a rubber tree per year. How many trees were tapped on rubber in 1986?

9   Elephants are used for timber work in Sri Lanka. An elephant can tug along a big log, 6.0 metres in length and with a diameter of 0.6 metres. What is the weight of such a log if the wood density is 0.9 kg/dm^3? Round off the result to tens of kilograms.

Volume of log $V = \pi \cdot r \cdot r \cdot h$. Use $\pi = 3.14$

SRI LANKA - A TRAVELLING DESTINATION

This is the Öster family

The Östers are planning a journey from Stockholm to Columbo. They will go by air via Copenhagen.

Dad   Mum   Richard   Lena
15 years   9 years

In a travel pamphlet they get the following information:

Köpenhamn-		Pris i kronor	
		Enkel	T&R
Köpenhamn-	Bombay	2895	5060
"	Delhi	2895	5060
"	Colombo	2615	5170
"	Maldiverna	2695	5175
"	Katmandu	3080	5885
"	Dhaka	2750	5445
"	Bangkok	2995	5550
"	Singapore	2970	5645
"	Kuala Lumpur	2695	5335
"	Manila	3465	6100
"	Peking	3465	6875
"	Tokyo	3575	6380

Köpenhamn
Peking
Katmandu   Dhaka
Tokyo
Karachi   Bangkok
Manila
Delhi   Singapore
Bombay   Kuala Lumpur
Colombo
Maldiverna

Children's reduction: 2-12 years 50%

Addtion: Connection Stockholm-Copenhagen 375 kronor (return ticket)

10   What is the return cost of the journey for the whole family? Observe the addition for
     the journey Stockholm- Copenhagen. No reduction is granted for that pert of the
     journey.

11   Mr Öster borrows 12 000 kronor in his bank for the journey. Every half year he
     pays off the loan with 1 000 kronor plus interest. The rate of interest is 15.5% How
     much is he to pay after the first half year?

12   Sri Lanka has a form which can be compared to the gable of a house. On the map,
     measure the distances you need and make an estimate of the area of Sri Lanka. Round
     off the result to thousands of square kilometres.

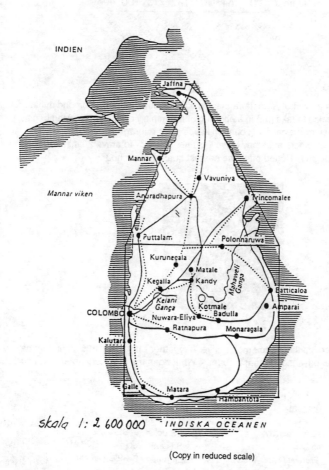

(Copy in reduced scale)

DISTANCES IN KILOMETERS

	Bentota	Colombo	Jaffna	Kandy	Nuwara Eliya	Ratnapura	Talaimannar
Talaimannar	406	340	246	264	341	365	0
Ratnapura	100	105	422	142	148	0	365
Nuwara Eliya	215	180	398	77	0	148	341
Kandy	182	116	320	0	77	142	264
Jaffna	462	396	0	320	398	422	246
Colombo	64	0	396	116	180	105	340
Bentota	0	64	462	182	215	100	406

13 Close to the town of Ratnapura there is a region known for its diamond mines. The Östers decide to take part in a showing of the mining area. The showing begins at 12.00. They rent a car and count on keeping an average speed of 25 km/h.
At the latest, when must they leave Columbo in order to arrive 20 minutes before the showing begins? Round off to the nearest quarter of an hour.

14 The Östers continue their motor drive. Altogether they travel 435 km in four days. Mrs Öster pays the car rent in rupees. What does the sum correspond to in Swedish kronor?

Car rent

70 rupies/day
and
8 rupies/ km

Rates of exchange

1 US dollar = SEK 6.27
1 Sri Lanka rupie = SEK 0.21
SEK means Swedish kronor

Index

263